JAPANESE FOLKTALES

JAPANESE FOLKTALES

STORIES ABOUT
JUDGE OOKA

Text by Věnceslava Hrdličková and Zdeněk Hrdlička
Illustrations by Denisa Wagnerová

Text by **Věnceslava Hrdličková and Zdeněk Hrdlička**
Translated by **Elynor Köppelová**
Edited by **Iris Lewitová**
Illustrations by **Denisa Wagnerová**
Graphic design by **Marta Sonnbergová**

Designed and produced by Aventinum
English language edition first published 1994 by
Sunburst Books, 65 Old Church Street, London SW3 5BS

© **Aventinum, Prague 1993**

ISBN 1 85778 031 0
Printed in the Slovak Republic
1/20/14/51-01

Contents

SOURCES

Much of the material was collected throughout the countryside where it was passed down by word of mouth. Tales about Ooka are told by Japanese story-tellers to this day.

WRITTEN SOURCES

Shinzo Oisi, OOKA ECHIZEN KAMI TADASUKE,
Iwanami Shoten, Tokyo 1980

Yoshikawa Eiji, OOKA ECHIZEN, Kodansha, Tokyo 1980

Introduction

We could begin like a fairy story – *Once upon a time there was a judge whose name was Ooka… The hero of our book was a real person, though one who did so many good deeds that tales about him are still being told today.*

Ooka lived in Japan during the time known as Edo (1615–1868). It got its name from the town of Edo, the seat of Shoguns of the Tokugawa family, the hereditary army commanders. The capital of the country was still the ancient town of Kyoto, where the Emperor lived in seclusion with his court. He kept his title and his honours, but he no longer had any power.

Although the country was very peaceful, the Tokugawa family imposed strict military discipline on the life of medieval Japan. The samurais, who were members of the privileged military class, carried two swords to keep everybody else in fear and obedience. They had the right to behead anybody who was careless enough to get in their way.

The Tokugawas feared the slightest sign of rebellion or foreign influence, and decided to isolate the islands of Japan from the rest of the world. Nobody was allowed to leave the Japanese islands, nor was anybody permitted to land there. They went so far as to stop building any ships that could go out to sea.

It is not surprising that in this atmosphere of oppression and cruelty people found consolation in stories and fairy tales in which wisdom and justice always overcame evil and tyranny. They expressed the people's longing and hopes for a dignified life without fear, and that is where the stories about Judge Ooka belong.

7

In Search of Truth and Justice

IN THE 17TH CENTURY the Tokugawa family came to power in Japan as the hereditary military rulers, the Shoguns. They promoted the well-known Ooka family to be their standard-bearer knights or *hatamots*.

Ooka Tadasuke was born in 1677 as the fourth son of a family which also had six daughters. As a child he was called Little Colt. Until he reached the age of ten he was happy and contented in his father's house, never thinking that anything could change in his life. One day, as he was playing with his brothers beneath a large tree in the garden, his mother came out and said, 'Little Colt, your father

wants to speak to you. He's waiting for you in his study.'

Her voice was so sad that he was surprised, but did not dare to ask any questions. Discipline in the standard-bearer knight's family was very strict, and the children had to obey their parents without question. Little Colt hurried to his father and when he reached the veranda of the study, he knelt before his father, touching the floor with his forehead.

His father asked him, 'Do you know your uncle Tadazane?'

'Yes,' Little Colt answered politely, wondering why his father was asking him such a question. He must know how familiar his uncle was to him.

'You will now become his son,' his father said without any explanation in a tone which brooked no objection.

At first Little Colt could not grasp what his father was telling him. After all he had his own parents and brothers and sisters, and loved them with all his heart. It had never occurred to him that he might have to leave them. However, he was afraid to ask the reason.

'You know, of course, that the first-born son always becomes the heir and the head of the family,' his father continued. 'You are the youngest of my four sons and there is not much of a future for you in this house. Your uncle has no son of his own and would like to make you his heir. Do you understand?'

'Yes,' the boy whispered, with a lump

in his throat. 'From now on you must look on your uncle as your father,' he heard his father say as though from a great distance. His eyes filled with tears.

'When am I to go?' he managed to ask after a short while.

'Tomorrow,' his father answered without any more ado.

'That's all I wanted to tell you. You may go now.'

If only I could change my fate, Little Colt thought as he tried in vain to fall asleep that night. He was not even ten years old, and already was to be separated from his parents. However much he thought about it, he just could not imagine that from tomorrow this pleasant house where he had been born and where he was familiar with every corner, would no longer be his home.

The sliding door creaked open and his mother looked in.

'You are very fortunate,' she whispered, her voice shaking with sobs. 'I will never forget you,' she added, and before Little Colt knew what was happening, she had disappeared.

The next day Little Colt was formally introduced to his new parents and a ceremony was held to recognize him as the son of Ooka Tadazane. His home was now his uncle's quiet house, and Little Colt, who was used to the merry company of his brothers and sisters, felt very lonely. Everything depressed him there and whenever possible he went running back home, even if it was only for a short while.

He was always warmly welcomed by his mother, but his father held himself aloof, according to the strict code of behaviour in which the most important thing in life was discipline and obedience, no matter what one's feelings might be.

Little Colt made every effort to love his new parents, but try as he would he could not manage it.

The days passed and soon summer came to an end, with the holiday called *Obon*, when everyone danced and sang in the streets of Edo. His new mother tied some sweet cakes into a small bundle and

sent Little Colt to visit his brothers and sisters.

The little boy happily took the bundle and ran home as fast as his legs would carry him. The day passed all too quickly under the family roof and as evening approached he had not the slightest thought of leaving. When all the sweet things he had eaten made him feel sick, it suited him admirably. He groaned and moaned, and his mother made him some herb tea and put him to bed. Her loving care soon drove his pains away. He curled up contentedly under the bed-clothes and was soon fast asleep. Just as he was dreaming the most beautiful dreams, he was awakened by footsteps and he saw his father's stern face above him.

'Get up and go home,' old Ooka ordered him.

'But he is sick...,' he heard his beloved mother's voice at the door.

'All the more reason why he should go home quickly,' his father insisted. 'When one is ill, one should go to one's own bed and not the bed of strangers.'

Strangers, strangers? The words rang in Little Colt's ears, but what could he do but get up and go?

He had already gone quite a distance, when he heard a voice calling, 'Wait, wait, Little Colt, I'll come with you.'

It was his oldest brother Tadashina. He had run out without his father's knowledge to keep Little Colt company a bit longer.

12

Ooka never forgot this incident as long as he lived and when he became a judge and an important official, he was always kind to children because he knew how sad they often felt without their parents being aware of it.

As Little Colt grew older he became interested in books, and his new parents to whom he had become accustomed were satisfied with him. Five years passed and his childhood was coming to an and. From his 15th birthday he was no longer called Little Colt but Ichijuro Tadasuke; he was an adult.

About this time dark clouds began to gather above the Ooka family, although nobody realized it. Everything seemed very promising and Ooka's eldest brother, Tadashina, was looked upon with great favour by the Shogun Tsunayoshi. Maybe only he knew how dangerous this was, for Tsunayoshi was known for his hot temper and fickle character. And indeed, one day honest and sincere Tadashina displeased him and in a fit of rage the Shogun sent him into exile on the deserted island of Hachijojima, from where there was no escape. It was the summer

of the sixth year of the Genroku period, that is to say 1693 in our calendar.

In these times punishment fell not only on the offender but on his whole family. Tadashina's father was immediately dismissed from his office and forbidden access to the Shogun. This meant that he could not even beg Tsunayoshi to pardon his son.

Ooka was now seventeen, and had grown up devoted to the military ruler, who held the fate of the whole country in his hands. Until now his faith in the Shogun's justice and wisdom had been unswerving. But he also knew his brother well and was convinced he could not be capable of wrongdoing. Yet his brother's fate had changed from one day to the next. From the glow of the Shogun's favour he had fallen into the dark abyss of disgrace.

Ooka was so disturbed by what had happened that he began to neglect his studies, roaming the whole day through the narrow streets of Edo and its noisy markets. There he saw how the most wretched people really lived. It was a strange world. For a single offending word any samurai could behead an ordinary man with impunity. The Shogun Tsunayoshi issued arbitrary orders and nobody dared oppose him. He was called the Dog Shogun, not only because he was born in the year of the Dog – every year in Japan is denoted by one of the twelve zodiac signs – but because he was so fond of dogs

14

he preferred them to humans. He issued a decree forbidding the killing of dogs, or other animals, even fish and birds. He hoped that this would bring him favour in the eyes of Buddha, and bless him with a male heir, for he had lost his only son as a small child. The punishment for disobeying the Shogun's order was explicit – death.

Whoever was caught killing a dog or any other animal forfeited his head. The Shogun went so far as to have all stray dogs in Edo rounded up; shelters were built for them, and at one time, as we learn from historical annals, several thousand dogs were looked after there. For the Japanese, however, the ban on killing fish and other sea creatures was a greater hardship, for these were an essential item of food. Fear spread from Edo throughout the islands, for if things went on like that, people were afraid they would die of hunger.

Although the people were angry, they were afraid to show it, for the Shogun's hirelings were watching everywhere.

Ooka shared the ordinary people's sufferings with them as if he were one of them. Often he and his friend Tiger Pine would walk past the dogs' homes, wondering what could be done to get the Shogun to withdraw his order. They could think of nothing, but the guards became suspicious of the two youths. One day they tried to climb over the fence and so the men followed them. The boys had

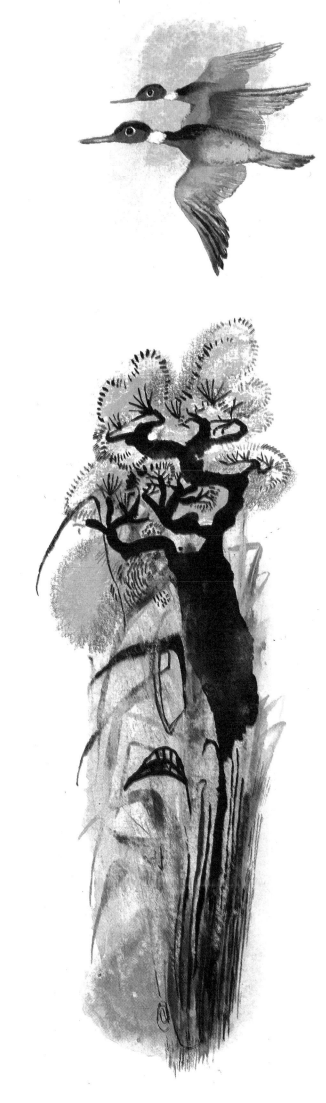

15

a narrow escape and took refuge in the poor quarter near the Willow Bridge. For several days Ooka was afraid to show himself at home and his parents searched for him far and wide. It looked as if he had disappeared into thin air. Meanwhile, this experience proved to be a better education than any books could have given him. He lived from hand to mouth, learned to speak like a labourer or tradesman, and even like a beggar. This valuable ex-perience helped him in later years, when men were brought before him accused of crimes, to understand them and judge their cases wisely.

In the end he went back to his adoptive parents and devoted himself to the study of ancient books, hoping to find consolation and enlightenment there.

Life went on and when Ooka's father died at the turn of the century in 1700, Tadasuke became the head of this branch

of the Ooka family. Though he was still very young, he was soon renowned for his abilities, his prudence and wisdom. People were already coming to him for advice and so it is not surprising that he was chosen as one of the guards of the inner chambers of the Shogun's palace.

A year passed and on 22nd November a terrible earthquake devastated Edo. Houses, battlements and bridges were destroyed and thousands of people met their death in the ruins. Fire spread

throughout the town and everywhere people were screaming and dogs were barking and howling.

During these terrible days Ooka carried out his duties with great acumen and courage. The Shogun, seeing how capable he was, gradually entrusted him with more important tasks.

When Ooka was thirty-six he was appointed Chief Judge and Mayor of the town of Yamada, on the east coast of Honshu island. There too he displayed a great sense of justice, realizing as he dealt with the cases before him, that the laws were too cruel. As it was not in his power to change the laws, he at least tried to get round them so as to mitigate the sufferings of those the Shogun's police brought to trial. Long before torture of the accused was officially abolished, Ooka had forbidden it, demanding evidence of crime, and allowing extenuating circumstances. He worked hard, and nothing was further from his nature than the cold indifference to the fate of those he dealt with, which was the common attitude among judiciary officials.

Ooka became popular with the people of Yamada. Soon his unusual sentences became known throughout the country and news of them reached Edo. Yoshimune, the future Shogun who was living on his father's estate in Yamada, also heard about Ooka.

After working in this region for four years, Ooka was recalled to Edo, where he was put in charge of the town's bridges, dikes and water supply. He improved the system of water pipes which had already been partly built in this medieval town, and did much more for the improvement of living conditions there than his office demanded.

Yoshimune soon became the eighth Shogun of the Tokugawa family, and began his rule by replacing all the high officials. Ooka was entrusted with the important office of *Machibugyo,* one of the two mayors of the town Edo, which already had nearly a million inhabitants. Ooka was also appointed to administer the law in court and on this occasion was named Prince of Echizen, by which name he is known to this day.

Ooka always insisted that every case must be thoroughly investigated and the court officials of Edo found this difficult. Ooka reflected upon each case for a long time before sentencing a man to such cruel punishment as burning at the stake or crucifixion. One day they brought before him a merchant who had unwittingly bought some stolen goods. The real culprit, the thief, had disappeared without a trace. As was the custom, the police bound the accused merchant and kept him prisoner in his home until he could be conveyed to court. This particular man had made up his mind to find the real thief at all costs. He broke his bonds and

19

set out, but before long he was caught. For this offence the penalty was hanging at the court gate as a warning to others.

Ooka examined the honest, terrified face of the accused for a long time. He listened to the witnesses, who confirmed that the man had always led an honest life.

'Are you Matsunoya Wasuke?' Ooka asked at last.

'Yes,' the merchant replied quietly, resigned to his fate.

'And where did it happen?'

The man looked at Ooka, not understanding why he was asking this question.

'Well, you fell down, didn't you? Where was that?'

The poor man still could not understand.

'…where did you fall down and break your bonds?'

At last the accused understood.

'I stumbled over the doorstep of my house, Your Excellency,' he managed to say, looking gratefully at Ooka, who had just saved his life.

The people of Edo had taken Ooka to their hearts for yet another reason. Not only was he an impartial judge, but he had formed a citizens' fire brigade for this timber-built town, which had been destroyed by fire more than once. In each quarter a tower was built from which watchmen gave warning of fire by ringing a bell.

Ooka was never satisfied with doing only what his duties demanded but put his whole heart into his work. He always tried to get to the bottom of things and to find a way of helping people in their misery. Because he wanted to know what really troubled them, he asked the Shogun to allow boxes to be placed at the town gates three times a month, into which people could throw notes with their complaints and wishes.

When he read them Ooka saw how much would have to be done to improve life in Edo. Again and again he saw what a catastrophe it was for poor people to fall sick. Often they had to steal in order to buy medicines for their children, wives, or aged parents. Those who lived alone died without any help, often worse off than a stray dog.

Ooka therefore decided to build a hospital in Edo, where treatment would be free. This was hard work but in the end he succeeded. The hospital was built in the Kanda quarter at a place called Ogawa and it was the first of its kind in the history of Japan.

After holding the position of *Machibugyo* for twenty years, Ooka was named Supreme Judge. This also brought all the great Japanese temples under his jurisdiction.

Ooka received many honours but he felt he was losing his strength, and in the autumn of 1751 he asked to be relieved of his duties. Soon afterwards he died at the age of seventy-five. He was buried in the family vault in the temple of Jogengi in Chigasaki, a town on the coast of the Pacific Ocean, in what is now Kanagawa province. To this day there are three days of festivities here every year in early April in memory of Ooka.

Processions are held, in medieval costumes, and the Fire Brigade always takes part, for Ooka is their patron. Visitors take away with them a reproduction of a valuable scroll which is kept in the temple. The calligraphic inscription is worth remembering, for it says: *Honour your wise men.*

Ooka and the Poacher of Noble Birth

THE STORY you will hear now dates from long ago, when Ooka was a judge in ancient Yamada. This meant that he had to say farewell to Edo for several years, which was not easy for him, for he was born in the city, it was part of his being and he had spent many happy as well as sad moments there. He knew it at the height of its beauty, when the sakura trees were in full bloom, when on clear days the miracle of snow-capped Fuji, Japan's most famous mountain, appeared on the horizon. Hardest of all was having to part with the plain-speaking, lively people of Edo, known as *Edokko*, 'children of Edo'. They could always be recognized

by the way they rolled their 'Rs' and by their carefree manners. Why should we worry about today, they used to say, when we don't know what tomorrow's wind will bring? They spent any money they earned the same day. They enjoyed life and the amusement stalls in the Ryo-goku quarter were always crowded on feast days and summer evenings.

However, now Ooka was ordered to Yamada by the Shogun and he had to obey. Ordinary people would travel on foot in those days, with a stick in their hands and their belongings in a sack on their backs, or in two bundles balanced on a stick over one shoulder. They trudged along rough roads and mere tracks, with only the grass for a pillow. Ooka was an important official, and so he travelled in a palanquin of black lacquer-ed wood decorated with gold and bearing the family coat of arms. He had an armed escort and his servants went in front bear-ing his insignia and carrying lanterns on which was written: 'By order of the Sho-gun.' They shouted at everybody to make way for their master. The chair bearers were specially chosen trained runners. They kept in step rhythmically to prevent the chair swinging from side to side, and causing the noble traveller discomfort. Even so, it was a long and tiring journey over dusty roads, crossing rivers by bridges, fords and ferries, going through mountain passes and along valleys, through busy towns and quiet villages,

24

not to mention deserted places where bandits lay in wait. Such men would not dare to attack the entourage of a High Official, however. The road Ooka followed was called Tokaido. It was the busiest road in the country, linking the imperial city of Kyoto with Edo. They turned off this main road at the little town of Yokkaichi and continued their journey along the beautiful sea coast.

At last, one day, Yamada appeared before them. It lay in lovely country banked up by rice fields covered in water. In the sun, reflected back from the water, the fields looked like dazzling mirrors. Above them, in the background, towered Mount Asama. Now and then the wind brought with it a salty whiff of sea air from the busy port of Toba. Fishermen's wives could be seen diving deep down into the calm water of the inlets, searching for pearl oysters.

Yamada greeted the new judge with all honours. Ooka looked at the crowd around him with interest. He sensed both curiosity and apprehension in their manner. And no wonder, for a high official such as he had unlimited power over the lives of the people throughout the region. If he turned out to be cruel and unjust, he could bring them much suffering.

The day after his arrival, before the sun has risen, Ooka was taken down to the seashore, to a place called Futamigaura. He wanted to see with his own eyes the two cliffs bound together with a strong

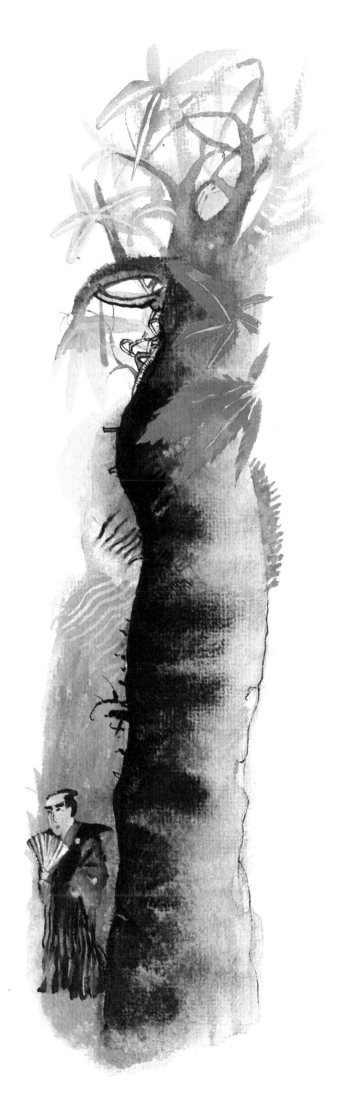

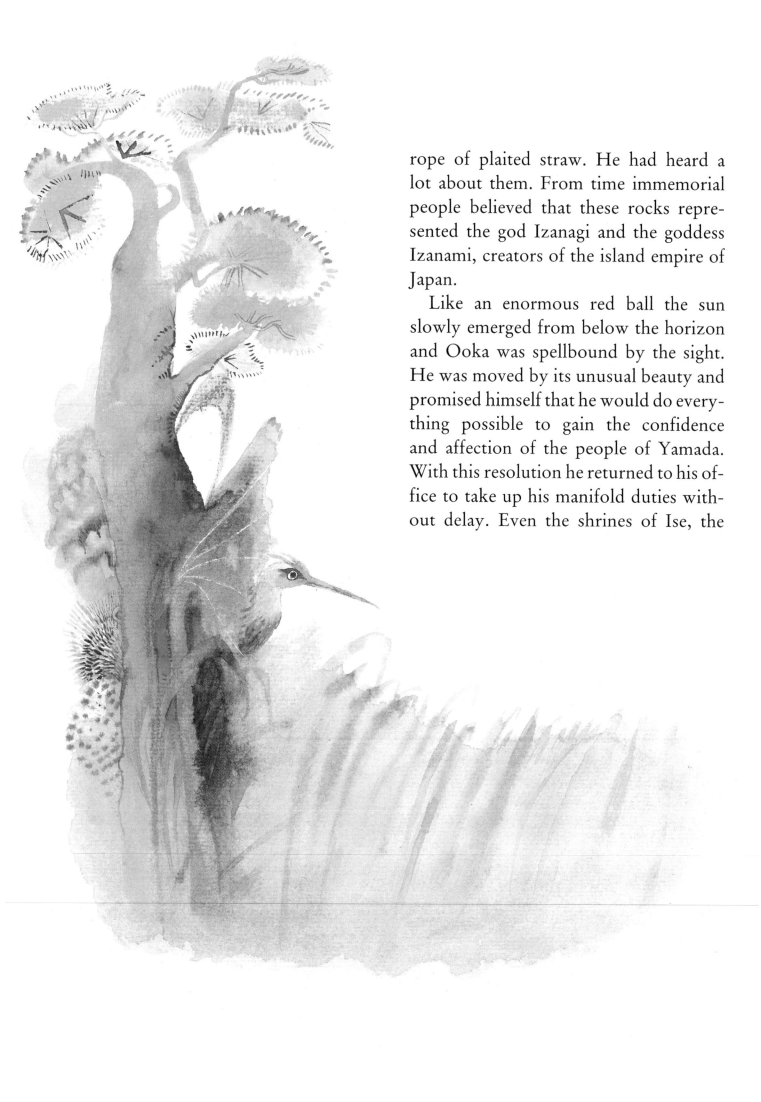

rope of plaited straw. He had heard a lot about them. From time immemorial people believed that these rocks represented the god Izanagi and the goddess Izanami, creators of the island empire of Japan.

Like an enormous red ball the sun slowly emerged from below the horizon and Ooka was spellbound by the sight. He was moved by its unusual beauty and promised himself that he would do everything possible to gain the confidence and affection of the people of Yamada. With this resolution he returned to his office to take up his manifold duties without delay. Even the shrines of Ise, the

most frequented by worshippers in the whole of Japan, lay within his jurisdiction. There is a song about these shrines in an old play telling that to see them only once in a lifetime is not enough; one should therefore be born a second time, to be able to return there. And that is indeed true! The buildings of unlacquered hinoki timber – the Japanese cypress – are very simple, and shine clear and immaculate from far away.

Since ancient times pilgrims from all corners of the country have been coming to the Shrines of Ise Jingu, as they are called. It meant many days and nights of travel through scorching heat and pour-

these is a round mirror, to which no ordinary person has access. It is said that long ago, when Amaterasu, the Goddess of the Sun, sent her grandson Ninigi down to Earth to rule over the islands that form Japan today, she gave him this mirror.

The shrines stand in an ancient park. Tiny lakes and pools rest in the shade of enormous trees. A holy quiet reigns there, for severe punishment would follow any disturbance of the peace. Yet believe it or not, a short time before Ooka came to Yamada, such a daredevil had appeared.

This was Yoshimune, a son of the powerful lord of Kii, a close relative of the Shogun Ienobu, who ruled the country at that time. Yoshimune was known for his warm-hearted but unruly nature. Although he was always quite willing to put things right again, often it was too late. Not that this bothered him unduly, for he knew how powerful his father was, and thought nothing could happen to him. He did as he liked wherever and whenever he wished.

His greatest passion was fishing. The rivers and lakes on his father's estates no longer satisfied him, and it was much more exciting to cross into the sacred park surrounding the shrines and fish in pools no other man would even approach, let alone cast his nets there. But Yoshimune and his friends behaved as if the whole place belonged to them, rowdily wading through the waters frighten-

ing rain, nothing but the straw sandals of pilgrims on their feet in the dust and mud. To show their lowliness and humility they lived only on alms from the hands of kind people along their way.

In the innermost sanctum of the shrine, behind many walls, lie the sacred treasures of the land. The most precious of ing the fish and scaring birds away. They came with their fishing rods and nets long before sunrise. The guards of the shrines saw them returning with their catch as the sun was rising, but they did not dare to stop them, though they knew they were failing in their duty.

Nothing remains secret for long and news of these highspirited expeditions reached the ears of the judge in office in Yamada at that time. Ooka's predecessor was getting on in age and preparing to retire, and wanted to have nothing to do with noble poachers, although he knew he should not tolerate such shocking misdeeds. True, he was deeply angered by such brazen behaviour, but he never showed it. To be quite frank, he was more concerned not to rouse the anger of the Lord of Kii, than to maintain order and justice, for this powerful noble worshipped his son and denied him nothing.

Soon after Ooka took up his office he heard about the poaching of the young nobleman and his companions. One of his confidential clerks told him this, hesitantly and evasively. 'Is this true? Have you any proof?' Ooka asked doubtfully.

'Yes, Your Honour, the shrine guards can testify to it!'

'Let everybody who is responsible for peace and order in the shrines come to me at once,' Ooka ordered.

'As you wish, Your Honour, but if I may give you a word of advice, be careful, for the Lord of Kii...' the clerk whispered to the judge.

'Save your breath now and instead of unnecessary talk carry out my orders!' Ooka interrupted him.

'Of course, of course, Your Honour. I just wanted you to be informed of everything,' the eager clerk mumbled, and quickly disappeared.

Sooner than an arrow could reach its target, all the guards and clerks were kneeling before Ooka, their heads touching the floor. The judge motioned them to rise and listen to what he had to say.

'You are no doubt all aware,' he said, looking round to make sure they were all listening, 'that as long as can be remembered, fishing in the park surrounding the Shrines of Ise has been forbidden. Anyone found fishing with a rod or net in any of these streams or pools will be severely punished according to the law. Keep good watch on these sacred places by day and night, and if you find anybody dis-

obeying this law, then bring him before me, whoever it may be. Now go back and do your duty.'

The clerks and guards were at a loss to understand what the new judge from Edo intended to do and why he was starting with the most difficult matter of all. Not one of them dreamed he would dare raise his hand against the son of the much-feared Lord of Kii.

'Let's wait and see what happens,' they said to each other. 'Probably nothing will come of it.'

When the aristocratic poachers set out again one fine morning to do some fishing in their favourite haunts, they could hardly believe their eyes when they suddenly found themselves surrounded by armed shrine guards.

In vain they tried to resist. Swearing and threatening was of no avail. They were brought before Ooka, Yoshimune included.

Instead of kneeling before him as was the custom, they remained standing defiantly. With a mocking sneer on their faces they waited without any sign of fear.

Ooka ordered them to come nearer. They did so unwillingly, and one even retorted angrily:

'How dare you, Judge, delay us for no reason? The guards who are responsible for bringing us here will be shorter by a head before the sun sets today.'

Ooka listened impassively, gazing at them sternly.

'Who are you to dare to flout the ban on fishing which is known to all not only on this part of the country, but the whole land? And to disturb the peace of the sacred waters of the Shrines of Ise!'

'Ha, ha, Judge, it's quite possible that your guards are stupid fools, who don't know the difference between an ordinary villager and a man of noble birth. No doubt you, who are an educated man, will see their mistake and put matters right when we tell you this,' pointing to a tall youth in their midst, 'is Yoshimune, the son of the Lord of Kii.'

Ooka looked at the self-confident youth questioningly. He tossed his head proudly, saying with a sneer, 'I am Yoshimune, if you are really not aware of it, Judge.'

His whole attitude implied that he was used to having his own way.

The boy's behaviour had no effect on Ooka. He looked him over from head to foot for a long time. The others grew quiet. They had never seen anyone, even a high official of the Shogun, treat Yoshimune with anything but exaggerated politeness.

Finally Ooka spoke, 'You are fortunate, my boy, for you really do resemble the youth you say you are. But, as my name is Ooka, I know for certain that you are a liar and a cheat.'

The judge fell silent and not a sound was heard in the room. All were waiting

hurl insults at the judge as was his habit. He bowed his head without a word and suddenly looked modest and uncomfortable. His friends had never seen him like that.

'You declare that you are Yoshimune,' Ooka continued. 'But everything points to impudent trickery. You are pretending to be the son of the Lord of Kii so as not to be held responsible for what you have done. You can't trick me so easily, I have seen many swindlers like you. Listen to me: You are accused not only of poaching, but also of deceiving the authorities.'

None of those present could believe their ears. Yoshimune a poacher and impostor? Ooka could not really mean that!

The new judge convinced them in no time that he was in earnest. He ordered the guards to take the poachers away and lock them up until further court proceedings.

While they were in prison Yoshimune's friends shouted insults and sneered at Ooka to pass their time away. They could not wait to see what the Lord of Kii would say to the judge when he heard about it all. The young men laughed loudly as they imagined how humiliated the judge would be and how meekly he would ask their forgiveness; they could be heard far and wide.

Yoshimune sat in a corner gloomily, without speaking a word to anybody. His companions did not disturb him, thinking he was planning how to take revenge

to see what would happen next. Did the judge not know it was playing with fire to offend the son of the Lord of Kii, whose word was law in this province?

'I repeat that you are a liar and impostor and I can easily prove it,' the judge repeated, banging the small table before him with his fist to stress his words. 'Everybody knows the Lord of Kii is an honourable and just man. No one can make me believe that the son and heir of such a man would wilfully disturb the peace of the sacred park of the Shrines of Ise just to amuse himself and his friends.'

Ooka stopped and looked gravely at the culprits. Yoshimune did not retort angrily as everybody expected, nor did he on the judge for his temerity. This time, however, they were wrong. Yoshimune had quite different things on his mind. He could still hear the judge's words, that it was impossible for a descendant of such a noble family to commit deeds he would be ashamed of.

At last the day came when Ooka ordered the poachers to be brought before him so that he could pronounce sentence.

'Your Judge must be mad to think he can pass sentence on us!' Yoshimune's companions shouted at the guards.

Their shouts and sneers were of no avail. The guards brought them before the judge and ordered them to kneel and bow their heads to the ground.

Yoshimune obeyed at once and the others had no alternative but follow him, however unwillingly.

The judge sat erect in his chair and looked very grave. The offenders suddenly realized that this judge was quite capable of punishing them. Was there nobody who could stop him?

The youths looked furtively at Yoshimune as if expecting an answer to their unspoken question, but the young nobleman knelt, with bowed head, without uttering a word. He gave no sign of what he was thinking. It was so quiet in the court that one could have heard a pin drop.

The judge was still silent and none of the offenders dared to look at him.

Finally the judge's gown-sleeves rust-led. Ooka opened his fan as a sign that the court procedure was about to begin.

They all realized that the situation was serious and that the moment had come when they would learn the judge's intentions.

Ooka cleared his throat and spoke: 'I have thought over your case for a long time. You have committed a grave offence. Breaking a law honoured by all the people of this country, whether they are old or young, deserves the most severe punishment. We all know this well. But because you stand before this court for the first time, I think that your imprisonment for several days is sufficient. If you should again wilfully dare to disturb the peace of the sacred Shrines, you will be punished with the utmost severity. The fact that you have deceived the court, however, is more serious. You know well that one of you pretended to be the son of the Lord of Kii, and by his behaviour disgraced the name of an innocent and honourable man. I have no doubt that if the Lord of Kii learned that a person as frivolous as you are,' and at this Ooka pointed his closed fan at Yoshimune, 'passed himself off as his son, you would at once be shorter by a head. All of you who abetted him in this deception are his accomplices. I therefore sentence you all to a fine of one gold piece each.'

The youths turned to Yoshimune, expecting him to protest. After all he really was the son of the Lord of Kii and not an impostor! Instead, Yoshimune bowed politely to Ooka and without a word opened his money-bag and laid ten gold pieces on the table.

'I hope this is the last time we meet here,' Ooka said in conclusion, setting the youths free.

Since then nobody has dared to disturb the peace of the Shrines of Ise.

The story goes on to say that Yoshimune never forgot this lesson. Not only did he bear the judge no grudge, but respected him deeply for his wisdom and justice.

After the ruling Shogun departed on that journey from which there is no return, he was succeeded by Yoshimune, who was his closest relative, as his own son had died at an early age. Yoshimune remembered Ooka and appointed him judge in Edo, giving him power to decide the fate of all who broke the law or committed crimes there.

A Faithful Servant's Confession

OOKA HAD already held office in Yamada for four years. He was greatly respected and in the whole province there was not a man or woman who did not know him or had heard about him. Unlike other highly placed officials of the Shogun, he was known to be incorruptible, just, and above all, wise. Honest people thought highly of him and thieves kept out of his way, moving elsewhere to be out of reach of his authority.

There was good order in the town and the neighbourhood and the people were content. They did not hesitate to come to the judge if there was anything troubling or displeasing them, and would ask him

for advice or help. They knew he had understanding for human weakness and that he would not cause unnecessary harm to anyone. He had a sense of humour, too, and his eyes would often twinkle.

When the people of Yamada learned that Ooka was to go to Edo, they were very sad.

'We will never have another judge like Ooka,' people would say to each other when they met at the well to draw water in the evening, where all the news of the town was discussed.

When Ooka left, the people of Yamada accompanied him far beyond the town gates.

'Don't forget Yamada!' they called after him as his sedan-chair was disappearing round a bend in the dusty road.

As usual Ooka's faithful servant Naosuke was with him. He was an active old man, slight in build. He had served the Ooka family for many years and had known his master from childhood. He was so devoted to Ooka that he would have sacrificed his life for him.

Naosuke was always up first in the morning, and in the evening he did not go to bed until he was sure all was in order in the house. On their journey to Edo, along roads crowded with the Emperor's couriers and soldiers, and innumerable suspicious characters who were not to be trusted, Naosuke was always close to his master, ready to protect him with his body if need be. He brewed fragrant green tea for the judge to quench his thirst and when they stopped at inns on the way, he made sure the bath was to his master's liking. When they came to a village called Yui, from which there was a beautiful view of Mount Fuji, he opened the sliding windows to enable Ooka to enjoy it.

Naosuke seemed to anticipate all Ooka's wishes, often carrying them out before the judge asked him.

When they finally reached Edo, they were soon engulfed by crowds in the streets. The famous Nihonbashi Bridge, from which since ancient times, all distances in the land were measured, was so crowded with people that Ooka and his retinue had to work their way through at a snail's pace.

The streets of Edo were the most colourful market under the sun. Narrators, puppet players and itinerant actors performed at crossroads and in temple courtyards. Pedlars sang and played different instruments to attract attention, some even dancing in the hope of selling their goods to the passers-by. Now and then quarrels broke out in the crowd, and all these sounds together caused such a din that it made one quite dizzy.

Ooka moved into a house some distance away, with a garden surrounded by a wall which kept the noise of the streets out. Autumn was just beginning and chrysanthemums of many different colours were in full bloom in the garden.

37

Ooka liked looking at their star-like flowers, especially in the morning when drops of dew were on their petals. Refreshed by this sight he would leave for his office where a great deal of work awaited him.

Ooka spent the first few months choosing his assistants, taking great care to employ people who were not only hard-working and clever, but also honest and just.

At the New Year, Ooka celebrated his accession to office with a banquet to which three hundred guests were invited.

The food was good and varied and the guests were being well entertained. When their cups of rice wine had been emptied many times and the feast was coming to an end, Ooka suddenly tapped his forehead with his fan and called: 'How could this have happened! I intended to offer my guests tangerines as a last course, and forgot to order them. Now, when they are ripening on the hills of Fujisawa and around Manazuru, they are at their best. I cannot let my guests miss such a delicacy. Fortunately there's still time to set things right.'

Ooka called the faithful Naosuke and ordered him to buy three hundred tangerines, one for each of his guests, and to bring them himself.

Naosuke bowed deeply and hurried off to carry out his master's order as quickly as possible. He soon returned with a basket full of lovely orange tangerines, picked that same day and still fragrant from the sun. Naosuke had been in such a hurry that he was quite out of breath. He put the basket at Ooka's feet saying, 'I have brought the tangerines as you asked me to. It took me a little longer because I took each of them in my hands to make sure I would bring the best. Excuse me for making you wait.'

'But you are back earlier than we expected,' Ooka praised him, bending down to inspect the fruit.

'They are beautiful, a real picture,' Ooka smiled.

The servant was about to hand the fruit to the guests when Ooka gestured to stop him.

'Wait, count them first,' he ordered.

Naosuke looked up in surprise, but without a word started to count – one, two, three …. putting the tangerines in rows on the mat so that everyone could admire their freshness and colour. When he came to number 298 he looked puzzled and after 299 he stopped.

The guests fell silent and looked at Naosuke, who was searching unhappily in the basket, to see if there wasn't another tangerine left there. In vain. The basket was empty and there was no tangerine.

'I told you to buy three hundred, one for each of my guests,' Ooka said to him gravely. 'How do you explain that there are only 299?'

'I can't explain it, my lord,' Naosuke was greatly disturbed. 'I know there were 300, I counted them myself. I took each one in my hand, to make sure none was damaged or rotten.'

'Nonsense. They looked so good your mouth watered and you ate one on the way. Confess, and nothing will happen to you.'

The servant looked around at the guests, who were watching and taking in every word that was being said. He turned red with shame and embarrassment and could not utter a word.

How can my master, who knows that I have served him faithfully all my life, suspect me of such a thing? he thought sadly.

'I did not eat one, I wouldn't dare!' he finally said almost inaudiably.

'Do you mean to say that a tangerine has legs and escaped from the basket all by itself?' Ooka said mockingly. 'There is no use denying it. You know you can't trick me.'

'I haven't taken anything, Your Honour,' the servant insisted, looking at his master in astonishment.

'If kindness won't do it, we'll have to be cruel,' the judge said in a threatening tone, which Naosuke had never heard him use. 'The matter must be investigated. What kind of a judge would I be if I couldn't prevent theft in my own house, though it is nothing more than a tangerine?'

Ooka nodded to one of the attendants and said, 'Bring your instruments and make sure he confesses.'

A wave of excitement swept over the room. No one had expected Ooka to carry the matter of a missing tangerine so far.

Naosuke thought that his master, who had always been kind and just to him, never saying a harsh word, must have gone mad. He trembled with terror at what would follow.

Soon the court assistants brought in the heavy wooden boards which were used at that time to crush the hands and feet of any unlucky person accused of an offence, to force him to confess. There was an iron brazier with red hot coals, as well as other instruments of torture.

They took hold of Naosuke and knocking him to his knees bound him with strong ropes so that he could not move. When he fainted at the sight of the terrible instruments they poured cold water over him to revive him.

It must be me who is mad, Naosuke thought. My master wouldn't do this to the biggest scoundrel under the sun he had ever to judge. Or am I dreaming it all?

'Set to!' Ooka ordered and the hangman's assistant stepped forward to torture Naosuke as they did in the prisons of the Edo shogunate all the time.

As the man lifted the red hot iron, Ooka turned to the accused once more, saying, 'Confess, before it is too late!'

'I confess,' Naosuke groaned, paralysed with fear at the sight of the terrible instruments of torture.

'Tell us everything that happened,' Ooka said to him, 'but I warn you, nothing but the truth.'

'I confess, my lord, Your Honour. As I was hurrying back I felt thirsty and wanted a tangerine so badly, that I ate one. I thought nobody would notice.'

There was a hum of amazement among the guests. 'You can't trust anybody today,' they whispered to one another.

'Such an old and faithul servant! He was like a member of the family and now he has turned out to be a thief. Who would have thought it?'

'Nothing escapes Ooka. We have never had such a judge in Edo before,' others said in approval. 'No wonder that they were so sad to see him leave Yamada.'

At that Ooka's voice could be heard once more, 'Then you admit before witnesses that you stole a tangerine?'

'Yes, Your Honour, I confess to everything,' Naosuke whispered with his head bent. 'Please punish me as a thief who has robbed his master deserves.'

Ooka was silent.

The guests grew silent, too.

After a while the judge nodded his head and there was sadness in his eyes. He turned to the servant bowed low before him and said gravely: 'My faithful Naosuke, forgive me for submitting you to such a test.' With these words he brought out the missing tangerine from the folds of his ceremonial gown.

Everybody gasped with amazement and hung on the judge's next words.

'Naosuke has never stolen anything, not even this tangerine,' Ooka continued. 'It was I who took it, in order to prove to you that fear of torture will force even an innocent person to confess to a crime he has not committed. Just imagine how many people have already been unjustly condemned in this way. That is why there is no place at my court for instruments of

41

torture. Take them away immediately!'

When his order has been obeyed, Ooka turned once more to those present: 'I beg you, friends, never to forget what you have just seen, when you are called upon to decide the fate of people accused of crime.'

Ooka kept his promise. Whatever the crime he was investigating, he never had anybody tortured. This was something unheard of in his day, and Ooka was centuries ahead of his time. This noble stand alone would have sufficed to make him an unforgettable figure in Japanese history.

The Boy and the Duck

Today I will tell you the story of something that happened shortly after Ooka was appointed Chief Judge in Edo. He wanted to familiarize himself with all the cases being tried, and as he read through the records, one case caught his attention. It was very recent.

The offender was a young fish pedlar called Yoshimatsu. On his way home the previous evening he walked along the moat surrounding the Shogun's castle. It was filled with water and a flock of wild ducks nested on the bank. At this time of year it was forbidden to kill a single duck – under pain of death. The boy was very hungry after spending the whole day

rushing around the town, and seeing the birds the vision of a tasty roast rose before his eyes. As it was already dark he thought nobody would see him. He picked up a stone, and threw it at one of the ducks as it flew up from the rushes. His aim was good and the bird fell to the ground. Yoshimatsu rushed to get it but just as he picked it up he was suddenly surrounded on all sides by guards. They bound him and took him to court, taking the dead duck with them.

When Ooka finished reading the report, he summoned the judge whose seal was on the document.

An elderly man appeared. His hair was already going grey and his step had long lost its youthful briskness. His face was expressionless and revealed nothing. He was in the formal dress of a Lower Judge of *Yoriki*. There were twenty-five such judges at the court of the South Town. They learned their duties from early youth, sitting at a respectful distance from the judge during court proceedings. Though the salary was low, their power was great. Like other Banner Knights they carried two swords in their belts and could use them to punish on the spot anyone who displeased them. Until Ooka took up office, the fate of all offenders lay in their hands and their decisions were never questioned.

44

Ooka showed the documents to the judge and asked him, 'What sentence is hanging over this boy?'

'Death,' was the brief answer. Without any more ado the judge prepared to leave, presuming the discussion had ended, but Ooka gestured for him to stay.

'How old is the lad?' he asked.

'Twelve.'

'Why does a child like that sell fish?'

'His father died when he was eight,' the Yoriki answered reluctantly. 'He has a mother and two sisters.'

'What about his mother?'

'She is ill and has been confined to bed for several years.'

'So the boy provides for her as well as the two sisters?'

'Yes, Your Honour,' the judge confirmed in a voice that showed surprise Ooka was making so much fuss about such a simple case.

'Is he to be sentenced to death?' Ooka asked.

'Yes, that is the law,' the judge replied coldly.

'Have the guards bring the boy here,' Ooka ordered.

'As you wish, Your Honour,' replied the Yoriki, bowing.

Before long the young offender knelt stiffly before Ooka on the white sand covering the courtyard.

'Is it true you have killed a duck?' Ooka asked him.

'Yes, Your Honour.'

'If that is so, then I want to see the duck, bring it here,' he told one of the court assistants waiting nearby. Two of them got up immediately to do as Ooka ordered.

Soon the duck was lying in front of the judge.

'Is this it?' asked Ooka, lifting the duck up so that the accused could see it.

'Yes, it is,' the boy answered.

'Are you sure it is the same one?'

'Yes.'

Ooka passed his hand over the duck's neck and said, 'But it is still warm!'

The boy looked up in surprise as if he could not believe his ears.

'See for yourself!' Ooka told the boy and handed him the duck. 'Now take it, and find somebody who will help you to bring it back to life.'

Yoshimatsu was quick to see what the

45

judge had in mind. He took the duck and ran as fast as his legs would carry him to Anjin poultry market. Here he found a live duck which looked exactly the same, and took it back to the court.

'There, you see, you have managed to bring it back to life,' Ooka smiled. 'The matter is settled. Go back to your mother and sisters and may you all live happily for a long time to come.'

When the boy told his family what had happened to him, in her joy his mother sat up in bed for the first time in years. From that moment her sickness gradually improved and before long she was quite well again.

Which Is the Real Mother?

IT WAS just before the Boys' Festival, which since ancient times has been held in Japan on the fifth day of the fifth month of the lunar calendar. Coloured flags and silk carp were fluttering on high masts above the roofs of Edo, proudly proclaiming male children in the house. The housewives were busy cleaning their homes and preparing the ceremonial bath for their sons. They put the sword-shaped leaves of bulrushes into the water, the symbol of boyhood. Besides, they are thought to keep away sickness and misfortune.

Ooka finally had some peace in his office because everybody was busy and the

47

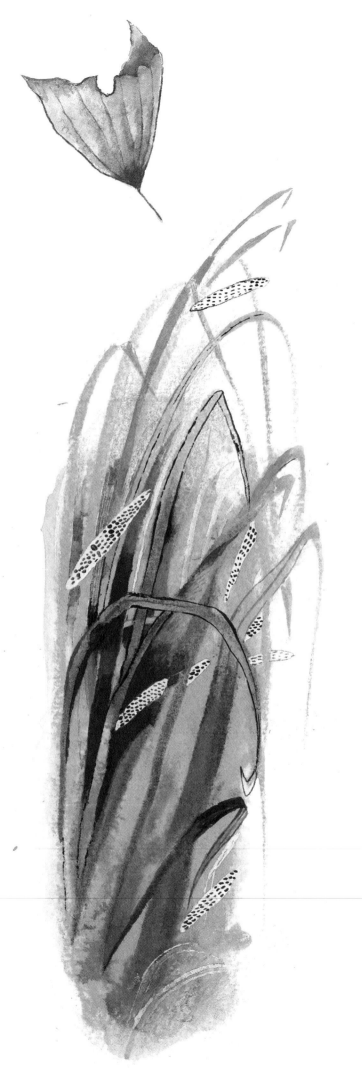

happiness of the coming feast led people to forget quarrels and disputes; he could 'hold his fan in his left hand,' as one says, meaning that he could use his right hand for something pleasant like drinking tea, for instance. Ooka was lifting a cup of this delicious beverage to his lips and was looking forward to enjoying it undisturbed. He has just been thinking, as he took the first sip, how the next day he would go for an early morning walk to the lake near his home, where irises of all colours grew, when sharp women's voices reached him from the street. He thought a child's sad sobs could be heard through the hubbub.

'What is going on?' Ooka called out to his servant.

'Oh, some women are quarrelling over a child,' Sansuke answered with a sigh. 'When will people have more sense and be kinder to one another, and let you have a little peace, sir? Shall I send them away, or will you listen to their plea?' he asked, adding, 'Their shoes are covered with dust. It looks as if they have come from the outskirts of the town.'

'I can't send them away when they have come such a long way with a child on the eve of a festive day. It must be a serious matter that has brought them here to ask me for my help,' Ooka said with a hardly audible sigh. He put his teacup aside, took the fan in his hand and went with solemn step to the court to take up his place on an elevated platform.

No sooner was he seated than the guards brought before him two women, holding a little boy of about five by the hand between them. Their hair was dishevelled and it was evident that they had come to blows.

'Don't forget where you are,' one of the guards reminded them. 'If you don't stop quarrelling and shouting at each other the judge will not listen to your case and he'll give you a fine.'

That had the necessary effect. The women were quiet, waiting respectfully for the judge to speak.

'What brings you here?' Ooka asked.

The two women fell to their knees at his feet crying out simultaneously,

'Please listen to us, Your Honour, and decide our case justly.'

'That's what I am here for,' Ooka answered. 'You seem to have a long journey behind you. Where have you come from?'

'We have come all the way from Shinagawa,' the smaller of the two women answered promptly; she was dressed in a blue and white patterned kimono. 'Senjiro here,' she said pointing to the crying boy, 'can hardly stand on his feet and I had to carry him half the way, at that.'

'And whose fault is that except your own?' the other woman who was a little older, said. 'If it weren't for your lies and inventions, we wouldn't have had to

trouble the judge. After all it is this poor child who is worst off, through no fault of his own.' She pushed the boy forward saying, 'Bow to the judge, Senjiro.'

The boy was frightened and started to cry again. It is said with good reason that a child's tears will soften any heart. Ooka

was readily moved by them for he always remembered his own childhood, far away from his own mother, when he often felt great need of her, and would shed tears in secret.

'Don't be afraid and come here to me,' Ooka spoke kindly to Senjiro. 'I won't hurt you. I am fond of children. What's that you've got in your hand?'

'A tor-tor-toise,' Senjiro stammered, opening his hand to show the judge his clay toy.

'It is very nice, looks quite alive,' Ooka said, admiring it sincerely. 'Who gave it to you?'

'He got it from me,' the woman in the blue kimono spoke up. 'I am his mother, after all.'

'How can you say that?' the other snapped at her. She would have gone on but Ooka stopped her sternly.

'If you start quarrelling, I will have you thrown out. You'd better tell me what this is all about.'

'Allow me, Your Honour, to give you an explanation,' the woman in the blue kimono broke in forcefully, elbowing the other aside.

'Let the one who is the elder start,' Ooka decided.

'I am,' her rival announced. 'But only by a few days,' she added quickly, anxious not to make a false impression in such a sensitive matter for a woman.

'Then it is your turn to speak,' Ooka bade her.

'My name is Otei, sir,' the woman smoothed her untidy hair with her hand as she bowed. 'And she is Takao. Each of us gave birth to a boy five years ago. Because Takao had no milk, she asked me to nurse her baby with mine and to look after it. However, after a time her boy fell sick and departed this world.'

'That isn't true!' Takao cried out. 'She is lying. It was her child, not mine. She wants to take away my only comfort in my old age.'

'Then you both insist that you are the true mother of this child,' Ooka guessed.

'He is mine!' they both cried out with one voice, as if rehearsed.

'You want me to settle your dispute, is that it?'

'Yes, you alone can do that,' they agreed on that point, at least.

'Well, that is certainly not an easy task,' Ooka sighed. 'It is my duty, however, to judge all disputes without any exception. I must, therefore, deal with this case, of which nobody knows more details than you two. You are putting a heavy responsibility on me. After all, the one who will bear the consequences is this boy, Senjiro, who has no responsibility in the matter at all,' Ooka paused.

'Are you sure you don't want to reconsider it?' he asked.

'She is lying!' the two women cried, pointing to one another with hatred in their eyes.

'Silence!' Ooka said sternly. 'And you,

Senjiro, come here to me!' he nodded to the boy, who started crying again.

'Now, dry your tears and tell me if you know any songs.'

'I know, and a lot!' the boy said, his self-confidence returning, and stopped crying.

'If you sing for me I will send the servant to buy you something good to eat.'

The boy, who was hungry after the journey, smiled with joy. 'What about this one?' he said and started singing.

She went to buy some oil, capi, cap, hey!
She bought some oil, capi, cap, hey!
Then she slipped and the oil was gone,
Capi, cap, hey!

'You are a clever boy,' Ooka patted his head and sent the servant to a nearby shop to buy some sweets.

Then he turned to Takao and Otei saying, 'As you see, even foolish parents can have bright children, but now let us come to the matter at hand. When people are disputing ownership of a field, I order them to divide it in two. That can't be done with a child and certainly you would not want that. Such justice would lead nowhere.'

Ooka bowed his head and toyed silently with his fan.

'Listen, Otei,' he asked suddenly. 'Did your boy have any special birth-mark when he was born?'

'A special birth-mark?' the woman repeated in surprise, but quickly recovered herself and said. 'Yes, he was the sweetest child on earth.'

'And your child, Takao?'

'He was so clever and so lively, no other child could equal him,' Takao replied without hesitation.

'This won't get us very far,' Ooka sighed to himself, looking at the fan in his hand. 'I might have known. All mothers

53

are the same. I will have to try a different approach, but which one?'

Just then the servant came running back with a rice cake wrapped in an oak leaf. This was a favourite sweet with children during the boys' feast. Senjiro started to eat at once, while everyone watched him enjoying it.

'Poor boy, he must have been very hungry,' a market woman, with a face as round as a melon and an apron tied round her large body expressed her opinion, as she pushed to the front. 'And those two women are quarrelling over who gave birth to him instead of giving him some- thing to eat. It stands to reason that a child can't have two mothers. If I were the judge I would give them a good telling off!'

Ooka was glad of a few moments res- pite to think the matter over, and let the people discuss the unusual dispute among themselves.

When the discussion got too noisy, though, he raised his head and called out: 'Remember you are in court and not at the market! Behave yourselves accord- ingly!'

The people respected the judge greatly and stopped talking at once. It became quiet in the courtyard.

'Watching Senjiro I am not surprised you would both like him to be your son,' Ooka said, and from the tone of his voice one could tell that he already knew how to settle the quarrel. 'He is a fine, bright boy. When he grows up he will be the pride and support of his mother.'

'What more could parents wish for!' an elderly woman in the crowd sighed.

Ooka pretended not to hear the remark and continued:

'To settle this dispute justly, I must put you to the test. Otei, you take Senjiro by the right hand and you, Takao, by the left hand and each of you try to pull him to your side. The one who gets him to her first will be the winner. Start when I give the sign.'

The two women, one of whom was undoubtedly Senjiro's real mother while the other only pretended to be, looked at Ooka in surprise. Neither of them was very willing to comply. Yet, neither wanted to give in, and so they had to obey.

'Are you ready?' Ooka asked.

'Yes,' they both nodded.

'Then begin!'

The women started to pull the boy with as much strength as they could muster. Poor Senjiro! They nearly pulled his arms out of their sockets.

'Ow, ow, that hurts!' the boy began to cry. 'Let me go! I can't stand it!'

When Otei heard him, she instantly dropped his arm. Takao took advantage of this and pulled the boy to her side, her face lit up in triumph.

Ooka looked at her and then turned to Otei: 'You have lost,' he said.

'Oh, I know that! But it wasn't because I lack the strength, Your Honour. When I heard the boy crying and saw how it was hurting him, I felt so terribly sorry for him. I let him go rather than hurt him any more, although I knew it meant I would lose him,' Otei wept.

'You have lost the contest of strength,' Ooka told her. 'But you have won a much more important one. When you let the child go, you proved that you loved him more than anything, and that you were willing to make a great sacrifice for his sake.'

Ooka paused, then standing up he instructed the court scribe: 'Write now what I say. The verdict is, Senjiro's true mother is Otei.'

When the boy heard it he ran to her and put his arms around her, crying happily, 'Mother!'

'My own child!' said Otei, recovering from her surprise, and embraced the boy with tears in her eyes.

55

Ooka and all the others watched them, greatly moved. Even the court scribe, who had seen all kinds of happenings at court, was affected. He sat with the brush in his hand and forgot to write the verdict. When he realized Ooka was looking at him he started to write as fast as his fingers would go.

When Takao disappeared from the court, nobody even noticed she had gone.

The Antique Shop Robbery

AT THIS TIME Japan was enjoying a period of peace but the rulers were warriors and swords were greatly valued, not only for their richly decorated sword-guards and hilts, but above all for their perfect blades. Famous sword makers like Yoshimitsu, Masamune and Yoshihiro were highly esteemed throughout the country and high prices were paid for their work. It so happened that one day an antique-dealer moved to Edo from the imperial city of Kyoto. He opened a shop in a narrow street called Six Trees Street. He wanted to impress people and so he made it known that he had a collection of valuable swords. The truth was that he

really did have a very valuable weapon in his collection. It was a sword made by the famous craftsman Masamune.

Soon it was well known that the otherwise modest antique shop housed a real treasure. Rumours spread all over the town, and even travellers spending the night at one of the small inns in the town would talk about the rare sword. At one of the mountain inns at Hakone, near the Great Lake, a robber from Edo called Yoshiro heard about the valuable weapon. He was not just one of those small-time highwaymen found in large numbers on the roads between Edo and the capital Kyoto. He had committed so many crimes that there was a price on his head. He lived in the forests and only moved among people disguised as a charcoal burner.

When he heard what the travellers were saying about the antique dealer's treasure he grew very excited and his eyes sparkled with greed: Yoshiro loved swords above all else in the world. This made him forget his caution and he soon joined in the conversation.

'That must be a wonderful piece of work, a sword made by Masamune. What wouldn't I give just for a glance at it!'

'You aren't the only one,' remarked a servant who was accompanying a rich daimyo on the long trip from Edo to Kyoto, 'but it isn't as easy as all that. My master heard about the sword too, and went at once to the shop at Six Trees

Street. There were plenty of swords there, but not one of them was made by Masamune. It wasn't until he learned who my master was that the dealer took him into the back room. There on a black lacquered stand in a recess, was a sword in a beautiful sheath. My master drew it out to examine the blade, and just imagine, there was the name of the famous sword maker engraved on it!' The servant talked as though he had seen it with his own eyes. 'The edge of the blade was perfectly sharp, although General Oribe, whose sword it was, had cut a stone in two with it. All this is true, for my master told me about it.'

'Go on, what then? What happened then?' Yoshiro urged him. 'Has your master got the sword with him?'

'Goodness, no! He didn't buy it,' the servant said. 'The antique-dealer asked too high a price. Not even my master could pay so much, and he isn't a poor man.'

'That means the sword is in Edo,' Yoshiro remarked, his voice shaking with suppressed excitement.

'In the antique-dealer's bedroom,' confirmed the servant. 'Where else would it be?'

Yoshiro could wait no longer. That same night he set out for Edo. He ran most of the way, spurred on by his vision of the booty. He was lucky nobody took any notice of him and he reached the town before noon the following day.

He hid near the antique shop till dark, to get a good look round. He then planned how he would get into the bedroom and carry out the robbery.

It was already very late when the dealer's servant closed the shutters and fastened the door. All was quiet. Only the monotonous murmur of the tiny stream came from the garden waterfall. Now and then an owl hooted or a bat fluttered past.

The pale light of a night lamp gleamed in the narrow gap in the shutters. Yoshiro crept quietly to the window and pressed his ear to it. From inside he could hear the old man's regular deep breathing. The robber took a few more careful steps, slipped through the partly open door on to the terrace, and from there stole into the bedroom. Tiptoeing round the antique-dealer's bed he came to the recess where the sword made by the master craftsman Masamune rested on its stand. Everything would have passed off smoothly if Yoshiro, blinded by his longing to get the unique weapon, had not forgotten his caution. A quick movement of his hand knocked over the stand. The noise woke the dealer, who like most old people slept lightly. When he saw a strange figure in his room, he tried to jump out of bed, but Yoshiro was quicker. He drew the sword, swinging his arm ready to strike the man, but forgot how low the ceiling was. The sword hit the ceiling and fell from his hand. Yoshiro did not lose his wits and struck the man in the face with his fist. As he fell to the ground unconscious, the antique-dealer cried out. His cry cut through the silence of the night like a sharp knife and was heard by the police watch which was just patrolling Six Trees Street.

The police immediately ran into the house. Yoshiro left the sword lying on the floor, ran into the yard and jumped over the wall. He escaped by a hair's breadth, but knew he was not safe yet. When he imagined what fate awaited him if he were caught, he ran like a madman. He had already gone a good way and thought he was safe, when he fell right into the arms of other watchmen. His haste seemed suspicious to the men of law and so they halted him. Shining the police lantern on his face, one of them recognized him as the bandit for whose arrest a reward had been offered.

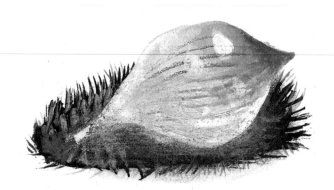

'I am sure it is Yoshiro. There is a price on his head and we have been searching for him over half a year. He disappeared without a trace and suddenly he falls right into our hands. He is certainly the man who broke into the antique shop in Six Trees Street and wounded the dealer,' the policeman insisted.

'Are there any witnesses?' Ooka asked. 'Did anybody see him there?'

'No, the old man only had a glimpse of him before he lost consciousness and since then he has been ill in bed. Today he is at last a little better.'

'Send for him,' Ooka commanded.

'Yes, we will do so at once,' the police commander answered, bowing, and added: 'Don't be deceived by this rogue,

A few days later Yoshiro was kneeling in the court room in front of Ooka. In his mind he reproached himself for what his carelessness and greed had got him into. But it was too late now! When Ooka asked him, 'What is your name?' it occurred to him that maybe he still had a chance. He was just about to say his true name when he thought better of it.

'Zentaro, Your Honour,' he lied.

'Zen-ta-ro,' the clerk spelled it out as he wrote the characters slowly in the record.

'He is lying!' one of the policemen shouted. 'His name is Yoshiro! I recognized him by this scar,' and he pointed to a red scar running across the whole of the bandit's right cheek.

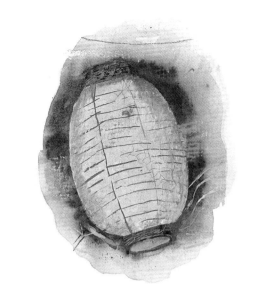

Your Honour. He knows he is in trouble and is using a false name. I would wager my head that it is Yoshiro, called the Killer!'

'That's not true,' Yoshiro cried when he heard him. 'I have been earning my living burning charcoal all my life and I live in the Hakone mountains. This is the first time I've been in Edo. Now I know I should have never come here but it is too late. It is all the fault of this cursed scar. I got it in a fight when I was a boy. Since then people have always been afraid of me, thinking I was a robber. I don't know why I, an honest man, should be so unfortunate.'

'You know how to talk, there's no doubt about that. Your words would melt a heart of stone,' Ooka said and a smile crossed his face. 'Who knows what really happened, but unless we find

some witnesses, I will have to set you free. After all, I can't punish a man only because he has a scar like a dangerous robber.'

No sooner had he said this than the wounded antique-dealer was brought into the courtroom. His head was bandaged and he was supported on each side by an attendant.

'Is this the man who attacked and wounded you?' Ooka pointed to the accused.

'It is hard to say, Your Honour,' the old man answered. 'I was so upset, I didn't much notice what the thief looked like.'

'Then there's nothing for it,' Ooka sighed after a moment's thought. 'We'll have to let you go after all, Zentaro. You also have the right to compensation for wrongful detention.' Ooka took four golden pieces out of his bag, tossing them

from hand to hand and showing them to the accused.

'Hold out your hand,' he said to him.

The robber's face lit up. At least some compensation for his bad luck, he thought, and stretched out his hand. Ooka took a coin between two fingers, held it for a moment before the robber's eyes and then slowly dropped it into his hand.

The robber quickly put it in his pocket and held out his hand for more, but Ooka put the remaining coins into the sleeve of his gown as if he had changed his mind.

'That's enough for today. I will let you have the rest tomorrow. You can go now.'

The robber bowed to the floor and with his head bent walked backwards towards the door.

'Yoshiro,' suddenly called the judge.

'Yes, Your Honour?'

'Yoshiro, if I give you the remaining three coins, what will you do with them?'

'You would really give them to me?' Yoshiro looked at Ooka in surprise.

'Yes, but I want to know what you will do with them.'

'What else would I do but buy the Eel's Inn in Fukugawa, if it is still for sale. I've my eyes on it for a long time,' the robber answered promptly.

'Hm, that will hardly be possible,' Ooka said sternly. 'Money is not much use for a man who is shorter by a head.'

'What do you mean, Your Honour?

You have nothing to convict me by,' the robber defended himself.

'There was no need. You have condemned yourself. Twice I called you, "Yoshiro" and each time you answered to that name, although you first declared you name was Zentaro. Besides, you said you were in Edo for the first time, yet you know such a remote place as the Eel's Inn at Fukugawa and even know it is for sale.'

The hardened robber was so surprised he stood in front of the judge with his mouth open like a shell thrown up on the seashore.

Ooka continued, 'It was you who attacked and wounded the antique-dealer, and for this crime and all the others you have committed, you will receive just punishment.'

And thus even a hardened robber like Yoshiro did not escape justice.

Ooka and the Two Honest Men

WITHIN a short time there was no-one in Edo who had not heard about Ooka. He was known to have a kind word for everybody and was always willing to help, and so people came to him with all their troubles.

Quite often it was a dispute over trifles that could have been settled with a little good will on both sides. However, we all know that human foolishness has no bounds. Ooka's courthouse was therefore very busy, and sobs and laughter were heard within its walls. Old and young would come, women with children on their backs complaining of their neighbours' misconduct; fishwives told

65

in shrill voices how they had been swindled by the merchant; swindlers caught red-handed swore that more honest men than they were hard to find.

The judge listened patiently to all of them though he often had more important matters on his mind. He knew it was not time wasted. Only in this way could he get to know the people, find out what they were really thinking and how they behaved when faced with problems in their lives. This often helped him to solve serious crimes that nobody knew how to deal with.

Each day, as Ooka left his quiet home for his busy office in the morning, he was ready to deal with all human problems and weaknesses. He thought there was nothing that could surprise him any more, and yet one day it happened. Believe it or not, they brought before him two honest men asking him to settle their dispute.

It is true that Ooka sometimes saw an honest man in court, but never before had he dealt with two men disputing which was the more honest, and going so far as to take the matter to court.

This is how it happened. On the outskirts of Edo, at a place called The Knoll in Shinjuku, there lived a man whose name was Saburobei. He worked from morning till night, carving little figures of the gods of good luck, in his workshop. Once a month he would wrap them in a bundle and take them to one of the markets round the Edo temples. There he spread them out on a mat, lit his pipe, and waited for customers. There was always a crowd of people around him. Everybody liked his figures very much but not many people had money to spare, and so he did not do much business. When New Year came around the gods Daikoku and Ebisu were the most sought after. Saburobei took great care when he carved these figures. He turned the soft wood about in his hands carefully for some time before starting to carve one of these two popular gods. Everybody believed that Daikoku, who had a smiling face and wore a flat cap on his head, brought happiness and riches to the home. He was also shown standing on two straw sacks of rice. Since time immemorial, that had been the guarantee of wealth. In his hand Daikoku held a mallet. It was said that if he struck the ground with it gold would come showering down.

If only that were true, Saburobei often sighed as the evening drew near and instead of being full of rice, his bowl and those of his wife and children were half empty.

Carving the god Ebisu gave Saburobei even greater pleasure. While this was in hand he forgot everything else and his chisel seemed to have wings. That was probably the reason why the face of this figure expressed such smiling good humour. Ebisu held a big fish under his arm, a fishing rod slung across his shoulder and was dressed in the formal clothes of

a clerk, quite out of place with the fishing tackle. But nobody could imagine him looking any different. A long time ago, so the legend says, really a very long time ago, he was born into a ruler's family. He was a good child and a happy one, and his father frequently asked him for advice when his head was spinning from all the problems of government.

One day when he again needed Ebisu, the servant could not find him anywhere. Finally they came upon him sitting on the bank of a lake in his formal clothes, with a fishing rod in his hand, enjoying the peaceful summer day. Since then he is always painted or carved with a rod in his hand, a fish under his arm and a smile on his face. This reminds people of his good nature and they worship him as the God of Happiness and Wealth. Fishermen and merchants consider him their patron.

Housewives used to place figures of both gods on a beam above the fireplace. They were often blackened by smoke but this took nothing away from their smiles.

One day a rich merchant from the Low Grass quarter came by and admired Saburobei's carved figurines. He ordered an exceptionally handsome statuette of Ebisu with the promise that, if the result satisfied him, he would pay three gold pieces for it. That was a good price for the poor woodcarver, for it was the end of the year and he had to pay all his debts, to start the new year with a clean slate, as was the ancient custom.

Saburobei set to work at once, choosing the best piece of wood he could find. His work went well, and maybe that was the reason why Ebisu looked so blissful. Everybody who set eyes on him was at once more cheerful, convinced that if no other, this god would surely bring good fortune.

Saburobei put the finished figurines in a bundle and walked through the whole of Edo to the Low Grass quarter where his customer Mr Jiroemon lived. He knocked at the side door. A servant opened it and took the carved figure from him, telling him that his master was not at home and that he would have to come next day for his money.

The carver did not dare to protest and returned home where his wife was already waiting for him anxiously, for she had no money left and not a grain of rice in the house. The children were crying from hunger.

'How glad I am to see you,' she welcomed him as soon as she heard the sound of his wooden sandals at the door.

'I haven't brought any money,' Saburobei said sadly.

'Mr Jiroemon wasn't at home.'

'Never mind. At least you have come back alive and well,' his wife answered. She knew how hard it was for her husband not to get his money and she did not want to make matters worse by reproaching him.

'Still worse, I left the carved figure

69

there,' the carver sighed. 'The servant took it from me before he told me his master was out. I am to call for my money tomorrow.'

'Well, it can't be helped. We'll manage until then. I'll borrow a handful of rice from the neighbours,' she consoled him. 'Let's hope he won't try to trick you saying he didn't get the figure. You know that the richer the customer, the harder it is to get money off him. Do you remember how the monastery last year refused to pay Tomooko from across the street for the fish the monks had been ordering from him the whole year long?'

'How could I forget,' Saburobei

brightened. 'They made all kinds of excuses but it was no use. In the end it came to court and Ooka showed them how they stood. They had to pay for everything and suffer the disgrace as well. Mr Jiroemon is not like that. He ordered the figure and I am sure he will pay up.'

The following day Saburobei got up at dawn and set off for the other end of Edo. The streets were still quite empty and seemed as drowsy as he himself felt. Only the servants of the samurais and noblemen were already out sweeping the pavements in front of their elegant houses. Pedlars appeared selling thick bean gruel in time for breakfast. Suddenly it started to rain and everybody hurried to find shelter. Only the woodcarver took no notice and ran as fast as his legs would carry him, until he reached Mr Jiroemon's house quite out of breath and soaking wet.

Like the previous day he announced himself at the side door. The servant recognized him at once. 'Oh, it's you, is it? You have bad luck, my master left a short while ago for his morning walk,' he said.

Saburobei was speechless. The rich merchant doesn't want to pay me and has told his servant to say he isn't in, he thought. When he had recovered a little, he answered miserably, 'Never mind. I will wait till he comes back!'

'Why wait,' the servant replied, 'the master has left you a package with three gold coins in it. I'll fetch it.'

Saburobei felt relieved. He would have his money after all and they would be able to celebrate New Year in happiness and comfort. At that moment he was convinced that at least one of the many gods he had carved in his lifetime was standing by him.

The servant soon returned with a scroll of white paper, inscribed with the words, 'To Saburobei, Master Carver from Shinjuku.'

'My master asked me to tell you he is very pleased with your carved figure and after the New Year he will also order one of Daikoku.'

The carver bowed and his hand trembled as he took the small packet from the servant. He tucked it into the sash of his jacket and set off joyfully for home. The streets were already full of people and Saburobei felt as if the whole world was smiling at him. He reached home tired but happy. His wife could tell afar that all was well, by the patter of his sandals. She opened the door quickly, prepared his slippers and began pouring tea for him as he sat down.

'You need to refresh yourself after your long journey. How did you manage to get back so quickly?' she asked cheerfully.

'I've got the money, after all,' Saburobei told her. 'Although Mr Jiroemon wasn't at home he left me the coins in a packet and after the New Year he is going to order a figure of Daikoku, too.

Here it is …' Saburobei reached for the packet in his sash, but it wasn't there. 'It's not possible,' he cried, 'that's where I put it, I am sure,' and he searched his sash, but the money just wasn't there. He untied the sash, shaking and inspecting it carefully once more. But he found nothing. The money wasn't there. He and his wife searched the passage, then in front of the house, and all around. It was as if the money had disappeared from the face of the earth.

'I'll go back, maybe I'll find it on the way,' said Saburobei and ran off. He nearly killed himself running head first into a pillar, because his eyes were fixed on the ground.

He did not get back home till the evening, worn out and empty-handed.

'Stop worrying,' his wife comforted him. 'I've still got a carved box that my mother left me. I'll take it to the pawnshop and pay our debts with what I get for it. There'll still be enough left for the New Year cakes. We weren't meant to have that money and I am sure it would not have brought us good luck.'

Saburobei looked at her gratefully. 'You are right,' he said. 'We'll get by without the money. The main thing is that we have good children and strong hands. I'll carve an even more beautiful figure and will get more than three gold coins for it.'

The carver went straight into his workshop, chose a suitable piece of wood, and set to work.

Meanwhile at the other end of Edo, near Jiroemon's house, there lived a man named Chojoro. He had a stall on wheels with the word 'Soba' painted on it, for that was the name of the noodles he sold. Throughout the year he lived from hand to mouth but now he was cheerful because trade would be good; these long noodles were traditionally eaten by everybody the last day of the year, so that good luck would last well into the new year.

And so no sooner was it light than he started to call out, 'O soba, O soba!' and the housewives, who liked Chojoro because he never swindled them, came running out to buy his goods. As the noodle-man passed from house to house, all at once he noticed a white packet lying on the ground, just the kind that was used for money.

He picked it up and carefully read the inscription: 'To Saburobei, Master Carver from Shinjuku.'

'Well, well. I wonder how much money there is inside', he thought to himself, feeling the packet with his fingers. 'There must be at least three gold pieces there. That's a lot of money for a poor man today. Hmm, Master Carver, that won't be anybody rich, and to lose so

much money just now, before the New Year, is really bad luck. He is sure to be in debt, and who isn't when everything is so expensive. I have debts, too, though I live alone and don't have a wife and children to feed. How nice it would be, though, to have three gold pieces! I would pay all my debts, get my best clothes from the pawnshop, and still have enough left to buy something extra.'

'Wake up, noodle-man!' a young housewife called to him. 'You're standing here as if you were moonstruck, mumbling to yourself.'

'That's all right, I was only resting,' the man replied.

Chojoro served his customer but then stopped his refrain of 'Noodles, buy my noodles'.

I'll drop everything and go and find Saburobei, he decided. I must give him his money. What if he has a large family to feed? A poor man doesn't steal from another poor man and I have never cheated anybody of a copper. What's his address? Shinjuku? That's the other end of the town. That's the end of trade for today. I'll make up for it tomorrow.

Chojoro left his barrow at home and set out to find the woodcarver; this was no easy matter. It was long past noon before he reached Shinjuku, and Shinjuku

was quite a big place. Trying to find a man named Saburobei there was no easier than looking for a needle in a haystack. Chojoro asked many people if they knew Saburobei, but everybody gave him different directions. One knew a Saburobei, but he wasn't a wood carver. Another knew a woodcarver, but his name wasn't Saburobei. It's hard to get sense out of some people, Chojoro thought. As it was getting dark there was nothing for it but to return home.

It looks as if tomorrow I won't make a copper either, he thought as he lay down to sleep. Anyway, I'll get up early and maybe I'll be lucky.

Next morning the housewives waited in vain for the noodle-man to appear. Looking round they wondered where he had got to. Meanwhile Chojoro was on his way to Shinjuku, but again he had no luck.

At last on the third day he happened to come to a place called the Knoll and on the house right in front of him there was a sign with the words: *Saburobei, Master Carver.*

'Hello, there,' he called at the door of the woodcarver's workshop. 'I'm Chojoro, the noodle-man, open the door, please.'

Saburobei came out and looked at the stranger in surprise. He did not look like a customer, he was dusty and shivering with cold, from walking the streets since early morning.

'What can I do for you?' he asked.

'I've brought you something,' Chojoro answered.

'I've no idea what that may be, but come in,' Saburobei cheerfully stood back to allow him to enter. 'I see you are trembling with cold. Have some hot tea. My wife has just made it to keep my fingers warm as I work. It is really very cold today.'

Chojoro was glad to accept the invitation. He sat at a low table on a square cushion and without any more ado laid the packet containing the three coins before the carver.

'Isn't this your money?' he asked him.

'It was, but I lost it,' the carver answered.

'Well, you've got it back. I found it near Mr Jiroemon's house.'

Chojoro pushed the packet towards the carver, but Saburobei did not touch it.

'Won't you check if it's all there?'

'Why should I? The money is yours, you found it,' the woodcarver said and pushed the packet back at the noodle-man.

'No, it's yours, it's in black and white that it belongs to you. You earned it honestly.'

'Yes, but I lost it. That shows fate didn't mean me to have it,' Saburobei retorted, unconvinced.

'This is your money,' the noodle-man said. 'There's no more to be said.' He was losing his patience.

75

'How many times must I tell you I don't want it. You found it, it's yours,' Saburobei, who was usually a friendly man, was getting angry.

Before long the men were quarrelling so heatedly that they were near fighting.

The carver's wife called her neighbours for help but to no avail. The two men would not stop quarrelling and pushing the packet of coins back and forth.

Things were getting serious, and somebody suggested that they go to Ooka, who would settle their argument justly.

The carver and the noodle-man agreed, but went on quarrelling the whole way, waving their arms about. By the time they reached the court there was quite a crowd with them.

'Let us in, we are looking for Judge Ooka!' one of the carver's neighbours cried, pushing the two angry men in with no care for the guards.

The woodcarver and the noodle-man went on arguing and shouting at each other, unaware of their surroundings. They only stopped when Ooka ordered them to be quiet.

'What is the cause of your dispute?' he asked.

When he heard the whole story his face lit up. 'Two honest men in court! That is a real miracle!' said Ooka, and asked the

carver who at that moment was holding the packet containing the money in his hands, to give it to him.

Saburobei complied and the judge took three shining gold pieces out of the white paper.

Now, how is our good judge going to settle things this time? the people who had piled into the courtroom wondered.

Those in front watched Ooka in surprise as he took out his own money-bag and added another gold coin to the three in his hand.

'Here are two coins for each of you,' he said, handing each man two coins.

'That settles your dispute. You can go!'

'You can't do this, Your Honour,' the noodle-man and the woodcarver began to speak at once after they recovered from their surprise.

'Why are you so surprised?' Ooka smiled. 'Each of us has lost one gold piece in this dispute. I was glad to add one gold piece of my own, because this is the first time I have met two such honest men. I wish you happiness and contentment for ten thousand years.'

We can only hope that the Judge's wish was fulfilled in part, for those two certainly deserved it.

The Horse That Talked

THE REIGN of the old year had ended and the New Year festivities had begun. There was not a cloud in the sky and the promise of spring could be felt in the air. The streets echoed with the cry, 'Ó medeto, ó medeto! All the best, all the best.' There was a festive mood in the town.

The court was peaceful, too. Disputes and quarrels had been put off until things returned to normal. Ooka was resting too, regaining strength for the coming year's work.

If only all the good wishes people exchange could be fulfilled, he thought, as he looked at the miniature plum tree in its bowl, covered in white flowers. No

household in Edo would be without this bonsai at this time of the year, for this fragile tree did not mind cold or snow and was, therefore, the symbol of perseverance and strength to resist even the hardest blows of fate.

New Year's Day was like a new birth. All the old had departed with the past, and the future was filled with hope. At least that is what people believed and why they could be carefree and happy.

Ooka wished he could relax and share in the festivities but this year he could not find peace. He could not get rid of the feeling that he had not fulfilled all the duties he had resolved to. Otherwise how could a dangerous criminal called The Tramp still be at large, although Ooka had ordered the most remote places to be searched, even the notorious Ryogoku quarter. The Tramp had simply disappeared from the face of the earth. It was most suspicious. He was a conspicuous figure who could scarcely escape the notice of the experienced town police. He was unusually strongly built, bearded and covered from head to foot in scars, evidence of his many fights.

Ooka suspected that The Tramp had escaped across the borders of the province in disguise. Perhaps he had forced a monk to add the Tramp's name to his passport as his guide; at that time it was not possible to travel through Japan without a passport.

His servant's low voice interrupted his

thoughts. 'Come in, Naosuke,' the judge bade him. 'What have you brought me? Good news, I hope, after all it's New Year!'

Kneeling in front of Ooka his servant replied, 'I can't say, sir. I came to tell you that a special messenger from Prince Maeda has just knocked at our gate, asking you to come to the house of his master urgently.'

'When, exactly?' asked Ooka, looking at the plum tree again.

'Hm, please don't be angry with me, but immediately, if possible,' Naosuke said reluctantly.

Ooka looked at his servant in surprise. It was certainly an unusual request during festival time.

'Did he bring a letter?'

'No, nothing, sir. Shall I bring him to you?' the servant asked.

'That isn't necessary. Let him tell the prince I am greatly honoured by the invitation and will come immediately,' Ooka said with his usual vigour and stood up. 'Tell the groom to prepare my white horse.'

Putting on his official robes Ooka mounted his horse and set out.

The streets were not so busy as on a weekday and before long Ooka was standing before the splendid red gate of the house where Prince Maeda always stayed when called to serve the Shogun in Edo for a time and had to leave his estate.

Ooka was expected and the prince's of-

ficers immediately led him to the reception hall, where the *Daimyo*, as the prince is called in Japanese, was waiting impatiently. Although his motionless face was like a mask, Ooka, an expert in reading human nature, noticed tremors of unrest in his eyes. The two men, one a high state offical, the other a hereditary nobleman, greeted each other according to protocol.

'I welcome you, Lord of Echizen,' Prince Maeda addressed Ooka by his aristocratic title. 'I apologize for disturbing you on a day which should be devoted to rest.'

'Your invitation is a great honour for me, sir,' Ooka bowed his head courteously. 'How can I be of service to you?'

'I want to ask your advice in an exceptional matter. You are known throughout the country for your great wisdom and justice and there is probably not one case you have not solved.'

'You flatter me, my lord. For in spite of all my efforts to bring order and safety to the town, I still owe the people of Edo a great deal,' Ooka answered with an involuntary sigh. 'But that is irrelevant. Please tell me how I can help you. I assure you I will do everything in my power.'

'As I have already said, this is an exceptional case, otherwise I would not have asked you to come all the way through the city to my humble home.' The *Daimyo* spoke with elegant courtesy. In fact one could see at once that this house was of outstanding elegance, which only a

very influential and wealthy person could afford.

'I had nothing particular to do and so was pleased to come,' Ooka answered, and thought that nobles, just like ordinary people, find every excuse not to come to terms with an unpleasant situation.

'Well, I'll come to the point, not to keep you too long,' the prince said, as if reading the judge's thoughts. 'You may have heard that I have an exceptionally fine horse, called Shige, which everybody in Edo envies me.'

Ooka shook his head to show that he knew nothing about the matter.

'Never mind,' the prince went on. 'You will have an opportunity to see him and I have no doubt you will agree. I have heard that you understand horses and that you settled the dispute between the Lord of Mito and the Lord of Satsuma justly when you decided how to divide the thirteen horses about which they were quarrelling?'

'You've heard about that, my lord?' Ooka smiled in surprise.

'Nothing remains a secret in Edo. You as Judge must know that. After all, in most cases it is only evil gossip that brings people to court,' the prince remarked bitterly.

'You are not far from the truth. Most cases are of a petty character. There are plenty of thieves and swindlers living in the town, not only honest people. However, that has nothing to do with this matter. I believe you wanted to say something about your finest horse?'

'Yes, yes... listen to this,' said the prince with a sigh, leaning towards the judge as if he didn't want anybody else to hear what they were discussing. 'This is nothing but the truth! Just imagine, this horse suddenly started to speak!' The prince was watching Ooka carefully to see how he would react to this statement.

Ooka's face remained calm. He showed neither surprise, disbelief or ridicule.

'Well, what do you think?' the prince asked, anxious to hear Ooka's opinion.

'Nothing, so far, sir. I have not seen it myself and would have to question at least one witness. Please don't think I doubt your word, but I am sure you will understand that...'

'Nothing is more simple,' the prince interrupted Ooka. 'I'll call the groom and he will confirm everything.'

The prince tapped his hand with his fan and a servant appeared.

'Send the groom Chosuke to me at once,' the prince ordered.

Before Ooka had time to appreciate and praise the dark brown ceremonial cup in which his frog-green tea was served, as a sign of the prince's respect, the clap-clap of shoes could be heard approaching and a sturdy man appeared in the doorway. He approached the prince on his knees not daring to look him in the face. It was not often that he would be called to the guest chamber.

'I have called you before Judge Ooka, Chosuke, to bear witness that the horse Shige, which is in your care, speaks like a human being.'

'I am happy to do so, my lord. Why not? It is the truth.' Turning to Judge Ooka Chosuke continued, 'I swear by the spirits of my ancestors that it isn't my fault, your Honour.'

'You are not accused of anything, Chosuke. After all you have been serving your master honestly for many years,' Ooka said to him in his kindly way, anxious to calm the frightened groom. 'But I need to know what happened. Can you tell me?'

'I would be glad to, honourable sir,' Chosuke said with relief in his voice. 'I shall never forget that morning. I went into the stable to feed Shige. I put some corn in his trough.'

The prince folded his fan impatiently so it crackled.

Chosuke understood at once what this meant. 'To cut things short,' he said hurriedly, faltering in the effort. 'I usually talk to the horses when I feed them.' He stopped suddenly, looking at his master for approval. 'There is nothing wrong in that, is there?'

'Of course not,' the prince replied. 'Go on,' he added in a calmer voice, as if ashamed for having shown impatience in front of Ooka, an unforgivable frailty for a nobleman.

'That morning I stroked Shige's mane,' the groom spoke as if he were just stroking the horse, and said to him, 'Today I will brush you down well for tomorrow you are taking your master to visit the Shogun. Your coat must shine like silk, you must be the most beautiful of all. When I said this, Shige stamped and I heard him say: "I always am, aren't I?" I jumped as if stabbed. Who is making fun of me? I thought, and searched the stable to see if there wasn't some joker hiding there. "You fool," Shige snorted angrily. "Who are you looking for?

Don't you realize that I'm speaking to you myself?" That is exactly how it was, sir,' the groom swore.

'Very well, I believe you. Did you inform your master?' Ooka asked him.

'No, I didn't. I was afraid he wouldn't believe me and would suspect me of having, er... had too much to drink.'

'It wouldn't be the first time,' the prince remarked sarcastically.

'I believe that you were as sober as you have ever been in your life,' the judge said with a hint of a smile. 'This doesn't seem a difficult matter. Shige the horse can talk.

It's an unusual thing but it isn't against the law. This is all I can say.' Ooka turned to the prince bowing gravely. 'That seems to be the end of it, sir. I will not hold you up any more and if you will permit…' Ooka prepared to leave.

'Please have patience,' the prince stopped. 'That isn't the end yet.'

'Did the horse say more than that? What else has happened?' said the judge, looking at the prince for an answer.

'Chosuke, continue and don't leave anything out,' the prince instructed the groom.

'As you wish, my lord,' the servant took a deep breath, as if it was going to last half a day, at least.

'Mind you keep to the point,' the prince admonished him.

'Yes, but where did I stop? Oh, yes… When I came to the stable that evening, I bowed to Shige three times and poured the best grain he had ever had into his trough. "Here's your supper," I said to him, "enjoy it." "Hm, I hope it's a proper meal at last," the horse replied. He whinnied contentedly: "This is better than the slop you usually feed me. Make sure I get this all the time from now on, or you'll get what's coming to you." You can see, sir, it's not easy being a groom,' Chosuke sighed sincerely.

'That I can believe,' Ooka said with a smile. 'It is no easier being a judge, either, especially when we have a horse like Shige in Edo.'

'Judge Ooka, does this testimony satisfy you?' the prince interrupted them with some irritation.

'Yes, it does,' Ooka replied.

'You may go, Chosuke,' the prince ordered and the groom left the room.

'I will tell you the rest myself, otherwise we will be sitting here until midnight,' said the prince. 'To cut a long story short, the next day I set out for the Shogun's palace with Shige to congratulate our supreme ruler at the New Year, together with other noblemen. Chosuke led the horse by the bridle with the stable master on the other side. When we came

to the gate I dismounted and entered on foot according to the custom.'

'Let me guess. Before you got back Shige let his tongue run away with him, as usually happens with such characters,' Ooka interrupted him.

'Yes, how did you know?' the prince asked in surprise.

'What else could one expect?' Ooka answered. 'What did he say?'

'I don't know how best to describe it. Maybe I should have let Chosuke tell it after all. Well he started to, hm, what should I say, grumble, that he wasn't going to stay there in such a dirty crowd and that it, excuse the word, stank worse there than in his stable and that his master… I had better not repeat it. In short, the worst gossip-monger in Edo would be artless compared to Shige.'

'What did people say?' asked Ooka.

'They enjoyed it better than theatrical performance!'

'I can imagine that!' Ooka found it hard to hide his smile.

'Just imagine, Ooka,' it was quite clear now that the prince had lost his usual composure and with it his dignified superiority, 'that somebody brought it all to the ears of the Shogun.'

'Brought what?'

'That I possess a horse that talks!'

'And the Shogun?'

'He commanded me to bring Shige to him tomorrow. He wants to convince himself that the horse really does talk, be-

87

cause it is something incredible. Yes, that was exactly what his order said.'

'And you are afraid, my lord, that the horse will speak ill of you before our illustrious ruler. Isn't that so?'

'Yes, because Shige talks like the worst guttersnipe! Whatever will the Shogun think?'

'That is really very serious. What do you intend to do?' Ooka asked anxiously.

'That is why I asked you to come here. I need your advice!' replied the prince with despair in his voice.

'This will be a hard nut to crack,' the judge bent his head, thinking hard. The prince watched, not daring to disturb him.

'The more I think about it the more I am convinced that there are dark forces at work. It is certainly unusual for a horse, which is not endowed with human abilities, to talk like a human being,' Ooka paused.

Suddenly he looked up: 'Have you not done great harm to somebody recently? Have you not caused a death, even unintentionally?'

'No, I am sure I have not,' the prince said promptly.

'Think it over carefully,' Ooka said. 'Are you sure one of your servants did not depart this world with a burden of hatred against you?'

'No, nothing like that has happened,' Prince Maeda insisted. 'All the people in my employ have served me loyally for

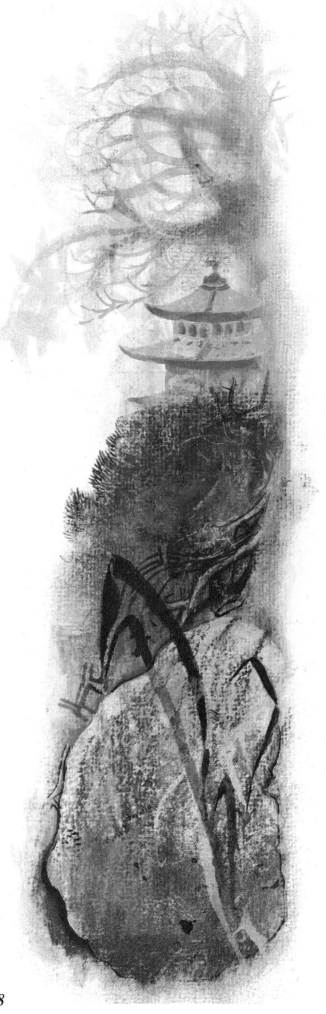

many years and I have had no reason to punish anybody and even less to take anyone's life.'

'Have there been any changes lately in the neighbourhood? Have you not disturbed the foundations of some building, or of a temple where human remains may have been buried?'

The prince did not answer at once.

'The only thing that occurs to me is this: There is a forsaken Fox temple near here. Nobody has worshipped there for a long time and it was falling to pieces. Before the New Year feast I decided to have it repaired, but the foundations were not disturbed.'

'That doesn't matter. Would it be possible to go and look at it?' Ooka suggested.

'Certainly, whatever you say,' the prince agreed.

The temple was close to the prince's house and at first sight it was apparent that its walls had been recently repaired. The roof, too, was shining new. As they crossed the courtyard, Ooka noticed a large boulder near an old well.

'Has that rock always been there?' he asked the prince.

'No. When the courtyard was cleared a pit full of brushwood and all kinds of rubbish was discovered. I told the men to cover it up with the boulder,' the prince explained.

'Could you have it removed and the pit cleared?' Ooka asked.

The prince looked at him in surprise but when he realized that it was meant more as an order than question, he agreed without hesitation.

He immediately sent for workers to bring strong rope and staves. After working hard for over an hour they managed to remove the boulder. Beneath it a pit yawned, with stone steps leading down.

'Bring some torches!' Ooka ordered, without hiding the excitement he felt.

'What are you going to do?' the prince asked anxiously.

'I will go down and find out what is concealed there,' Ooka answered.

'That could be dangerous,' the prince warned him.

'But we may find the key to this whole mystery,' Ooka would not be dissuaded.

'Do you mean to say...?' questioned the prince.

'I cannot say anything yet,' answered the judge, more harshly than was polite.

The servants hurried up with the torches. Ooka took off his outer garment and accompanied by the workers went down

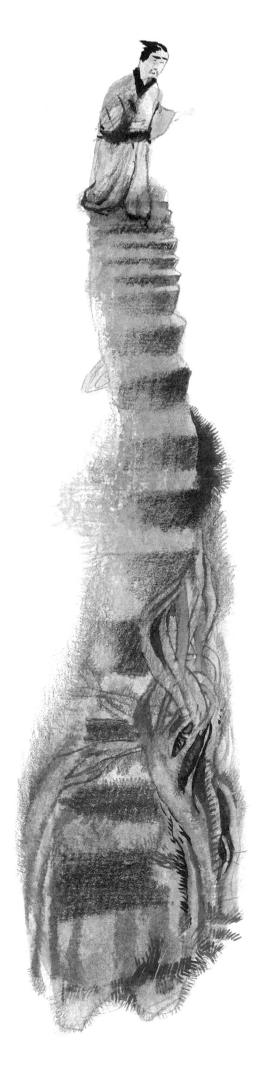

into the pit. The stone steps worked loose under their feet, they had to watch every step. Ooka felt as if something were dragging him inside and not even the unpleasant smell from within discouraged him.

When he reached the last step he saw before him a large cave. He took a few steps forward but the men with him hesitated. The judge took the torch from one of them and lit up the furthest corner which until then had been hidden in darkness.

The sight that met their eyes astonished them. On a plain bed an enormous bearded figure lay motionless, covered in scars. Ooka bent over him and cried out in amazement: 'The Tramp! Yes, it is he. So that's why nobody could find him!'

'Come here and look, judge! There is something written here,' said one of the men, plucking at Ooka's sleeve.

Ooka looked up. Above the bed, pinned to the wall with a dagger, was a piece of paper with some clumsily written characters on it.

'Hold the light up so that I can read it!' Ooka ordered.

A servant reluctantly came to the bed and raised his torch. In its flickering light the judge read with difficulty, 'I, Saido, called The Tramp, hereby curse Prince Maeda for blocking the way out from my hiding place with a boulder and thus condemning me to death. May misfortune befall him at every step. So be it!'

'This explains the mystery of the talking horse. The Tramp and his curse were behind it!' Ooka cried, tearing the paper from the wall.

'You two come back with me while the others search the place thoroughly,' Ooka ordered. 'I am sure you will find the bandit's booty hidden somewhere.'

The judge went quickly up the step to where the prince was waiting for him impatiently.

'Did you find anything?' he called, when Ooka emerged into the light of the day.

'First order your servants to prepare a purifying bath for me, because I have been in contact with a corpse. Then I will explain everything.'

When the judge had performed the purifying ceremony he told the prince, who was half dead from terror, what they have discovered in the cave.

'Then I am under a curse!' the prince groaned. 'What am I going to do? There is nothing left for me but die by my own hand!' the prince was already drawing one of the two swords tucked into his sash.

'Don't be in such a hurry, sir!' Ooka placed his hand on his shoulder. 'Life is too valuable to be thrown away without cause. Call a priest. If I burn the paper with The Tramp's curse and his seal on it in the presence of a priest, the evil spell will certainly lose its power and your horse will stop talking!'

Everything happened as Ooka had foreseen.

'You don't know, Honoured Judge, how grateful I am to you!' the prince said when everything was over. His words sounded unusually warm and sincere. 'How can I reward you? Please at least take the gold coins my servants found in the bandit's den.'

'Give them to the poor of Edo, so they too may celebrate the feast of the New Year in plenty and contentment. I have had my reward. After all, I have successfully solved a case that has been as heavy on my conscience as the boulder that blocked the entry to the cave.'

Ooka did not stay any longer in the prince's house but went home to enjoy at last the peace of the festive season.

After a time Ooka heard that the prince had obeyed the Shogun and had taken his horse to show him, but that the ruler could not make the animal say a single word. That convinced the great man that all the stories about a talking horse were only gossip, and so he allowed Prince Maeda to return home blameless.

A Debt Repaid

IN ONE of the narrow streets of old Edo lived a man called Shingobei. He earned his living frying fish dipped in a light batter of beaten eggs and flour, in sesame oil. This delicacy, *tempura*, has to be eaten the moment it comes out of pan. The smell of it is so tempting that even at a distance it makes one's mouth water.

Shingobei's shop was on the ground floor of his cottage. He had plenty of customers. People from the neighbourhood, passers-by and travellers from afar stopped there.

And rightly so! Dipped in a tart sauce Shingobei's *tempura* melted in one's mouth. No wonder his money chest was

94

full by the end of every evening. It was mostly copper coins with only a few gold pieces among them but to Shingobei, who loved money more than anything else in the world, even the tinkle of copper coins sounded like heavenly music. As you will have guessed, he was the biggest miser the world has ever seen.

Everything one hears about stingy people fitted him like a glove. Believe it or not, he was such a skinflint he would agree to anything to save a penny. If a splinter got under his skin, he'd pull it out and enter it in the 'received' column.

His only passion in life was to change his copper coins for gold. These were dearer to him than his own parents. He was so niggardly that he never even married. The idea that he would have to feed a wife and children made him feel quite faint.

Because he wanted to have more and more money in his chest he preferred to sleep uncomfortably in his narrow shop, and to let the upstairs garret. Nobody could stand his stinginess for long, but new tenants who did not know the circumstances could always be found.

One day the miser let the room to a student, Chohei, who was taking calligraphy lessons from a famous master living in the neighbouring quarter. Chohei wanted to learn to write beautifully so that he could become an official scribe and he had decided to devote his entire savings to that end.

He was a good tenant, quiet and polite and always paid on time. When he had paid his rent and bought some ink, paper and a brush, he had hardly anything left for food. However, that did not worry him, he was only concerned with learning. He was content with a bowl or two of rice every day.

Chohei used to rise early in the morning. As soon as it was light he washed at the well, drank some hot tea and set to work. He spread the ink and dipping his soft brush with its bamboo shaft in it started drawing the Japanese characters, which resemble pictures. When he had finished his task for the day he would visit the master to continue his studies under his tuition. Returning home late in the afternoon, he was always starving. After he had gulped down his daily ration of rice, he started work again. Often he practised his calligraphy until late into the night.

The stingy landlord followed his every step. There was nothing he could complain about, but in his heart of hearts he lamented the waste of ink and paper and the way his tenant used up precious brushes. He considered him an idler and a wastrel and barely returned his greeting.

One day Chohei's fellow student, Kamezo, came to visit him. They were from the same village and always had plenty to talk about.

'Are you hungry the whole time like me?' Kamezo suddenly asked his friend.

'Better not talk about it,' Chohei sighed, 'but I have made a discovery. I don't start to eat until my landlord starts frying fish in sesame oil. I eat my dry rice with my chopsticks and at the same time inhale the wonderful smell of *tempura*. When I've finished I have the feeling I've swallowed all the portions my landlord has fried. Wait here a while, he will start before long. I invite you to supper. We'll have rice and with it as good a smell of fried fish as you could wish for.' Kamezo accepted the invitation and was soon convinced that his friend spoke the truth.

'I haven't eaten so well, I mean sniffed so well, for a long time,' he said contentedly after supper. As he was leaving for home he bowed politely to Shingobei as if he wanted to thank him for letting him enjoy the fish, but the miser ignored his greeting and looked at him balefully. No wonder! In his room downstairs he had heard everything the two were saying upstairs. That was grist for his mill! The old skinflint! He was furious! The effort he put into making sure none of his neighbours or his customers robbed him of as much as a grain of rice – and now he had taken a thief into his own home!

A fine rascal Chohei has turned out to be! Shingobei raged. He looks so innocent, the cunning fellow, but he's as big a thief as they make them. Under my very nose he steals the smell of my tempura, and even invites his friend to have some too! What cheek! He ought to be ashamed to rob a poor man like me. I have to work like a horse to save a copper or two. All he does is daub his brush across the paper and lounge at the table instead of earning his living by honest work. Shingobei took out the small abacus without which no merchant in Edo could exist, and began

The student looked at him in surprise. 'Whatever do you mean, sir? I have paid my rent in advance as we agreed.'

'Who said I was talking about the rent?' Shingobei shouted even louder. 'You owe me for the smell of my fish fried in batter! You have been smelling it with your rice for the three months you've lived here. Make no mistake, I heard you praising it to your friend yes-

adding, subtracting, dividing and multiplying. He didn't stop until he had calculated how much Chohei owed him from the time he had come to live in his house. The result was ten coppers.

All that money! Shingobei banged his fist on the table in anger. When I imagine how nice those coppers would look in my money chest! What an old fool I have been to feed such a loafer free of charge, he thought to himself.

By now it was dark and Shingobei went to bed so he wouldn't have to light a candle. He could not fall asleep but kept tossing and turning all night. When morning came he had come to a decision. I won't let this rest, he thought. Either he pays up or I'll take him to court. They'll show him! Nobody is going to rob me. There must be justice somewhere.

That morning Chohei went to the well in the yard to wash as he did every day. The old miser stopped him and shouted:

'You owe me ten coppers! See that you don't keep me waiting!'

for the air that he breathes there,' Goro, the ragman, added his bit. He had some bad memories of the miser. Once, when he was buying some junk from Shingobei, the old man wanted as much for it as if it were new, and they had quarrelled bitterly about it.

terday, and you even invited him to have a free sniff, too!'

'You can't mean that seriously. Who ever heard of paying for a smell,' the student protested.

'Heard of it or not, that doesn't interest me. I want to know if you are ready to pay.'

'I'm not, where would I get the money from?' Chohei replied.

'Very well, if you don't pay then you will come with me to court!' the skinflint shouted.

A neighbour who was listening behind the fence, not to miss a word, ran straight to the rice shop opposite to tell them the news while it was fresh.

Soon there wasn't a soul in the neighbourhood who didn't know that Shingobei wanted his tenant to pay him ten coppers for the smell of his fried fish. They were all laughing at the miser till they nearly burst.

'Soon he will want to charge his tenant

99

'Look, they are going to court!' some- one cried out.

'We mustn't miss that. Let's go too!'

The women took off their aprons, left their washing and cooking; the men dropped their tools; tradesmen left their shops in the care of apprentices and all rushed after the student and his landlord, Shingobei, to the court. The ragman Goro limped after them laughing.

'Now the old miser will get what's coming to him. I can't wait to see it.'

At the court the miser made his com- plaint and Ooka listened carefully.

'Are there any witnesses?' he asked at last.

'You, Awayako, you heard every- thing,' the people pushed the landlord's fat neighbour forward. She did nothing else all day than watch what was going on in the street. She was known for her volu- bility, but now she stood as if she had been struck dumb.

'Is it true that the delicious smell of Shingobei frying fish reaches upstairs?' Ooka asked.

'Yes, Your Honour,' Awayako faltered out.

'Could the accused, Chohei, sniff it to his heart's content?'

'He could, Your Honour,' the woman nodded quickly.

'That's enough, thank you,' the judge said and in her confusion Awayako bow- ed to Chohei instead of Ooka and tried to get to the back of the crowd quickly.

'Then it appears that the fishfrier, Shingobei, is speaking the truth, and the witness has confirmed it. Now, Chohei, it's your turn,' the judge looked towards the student. 'Did you always sniff the smell of fish coming from the landlord's pan, when you were eating rice?'

'Yes, Your Honour, that's true,' the student answered politely. 'But that isn't...'

'Only answer my question,' the judge stopped him. 'Did you, or didn't you sniff?'

'Yes, I did,' said the student repeating his testimony.

'Then let us take things in the right order,' Ooka spoke again. 'The fish, the frying-pan and the oil belonged to Shingobei. Is that correct?'

'Yes, Your Honour, exactly as you say,' Shingobei hastened to confirm.

However, the judge paid no attention to him and continued.

'From that it is clear that the smell was his, too.'

When Ooka said this everybody gasped open-mouthed in surprise and soon there was as much noise there as in a beehive.

'Quiet, please. Then this means that the student Chohei, who is Mr Shingobei's tenant in Limping Cat Street, has been guilty of sniffing the smell of fish being fried by his landlord, without the latter's permission. It is evident from the case that it was a really wonderful smell.'

The old ragman, hearing this, could not help swallowing as his mouth watered, smacking his lips loudly. The others laughed but stopped at once when they heard the judge proclaiming in a grave voice: 'I sentence Chohei, kneeling here before me, to pay his landlord Shingobei ten coppers for the smell of this tempura, which he has sniffed for the three months while living in his house.'

'But, Your Honour, who ever heard of anyone paying just for the smell of food?' the student protested.

'Have you got ten coppers with you?' Ooka asked unemotionally.

'But if I pay, my purse will be empty and I will have nothing left to pay my rent or buy food until the end of the month. I will have to return home in shame.'

'Show me your money,' the judge bade him.

Chohei put his hand in his purse and

stretched his trembling hand towards the judge with the coins.

'Drop them from one hand to the other,' Ooka ordered.

Chohei obeyed and the coins tinkled merrily.

'Good,' the judge nodded his head and turned to Shingobei. 'Did you see the money?' he asked him.

'Yes, Your Honour,' the miser answered greedily.

'Is this the student Chohei's money?'

'Yes, Your Honour,' answered Shingobei.

'Did you hear it tinkle?'

The miser nodded.

'Then you have been paid and the dispute is settled. You can all go back home, you and your neighbours, too.'

'Your Honour, that must be a mistake, I haven't been paid,' the old skinflint protested angrily. As he heard the tempting

tinkle of the money in the student's hands he longed for it as strongly as the ragman longing for the *tempura* a short while before.

'What do you mean?' the judge asked in surprise and went on: 'Chohei paid for the smell of your fish with the tinkle of his money. What more do you want?'

There was laughter in the court. Everybody was pleased by the verdict but old Goro most of all.

Shingobei was so shamed by this court case that he had to move to another neighbourhood. No doubt if he is still alive he is hoarding money to this day.

Was Ooka Infallible?

THE JULY rainy season *tsuyu* had just begun and the weather in Edo was oppressive and damp. Soon a grey-green mould covered clothes, shoes and everything else stored in chests. Every so often it started to rain heavily and often it drizzled for hours on end. People had difficulty breathing and were irritable.

Early one evening, Hikobei, the pedlar, was returning from Ryogoku. He carried a heavy bundle on his back and was worn out from traipsing about all day. He had come to Edo the previous year from Osaka, which was several hundred miles away, where he had left his wife and two children. He had been tempted by reports that it was easier to earn a living in the Shogun's seat for in his native Osaka his family lived from hand to mouth. Life was not easy for him in Edo. He missed his family a great deal, but he told himself he had to endure it for a little while longer. If things went well with him he could save some money and buy his own shop in Osaka.

Thoughts like that were occupying his mind as he hurried through the streets of Edo. Suddenly it started to rain cats and dogs. Hikobei was in the Horse Trough Quarter. He had to take shelter under the eaves of the nearest house so as not to get soaked to the skin.

As he was standing there, a window opened and an elderly woman looked out. She observed him closely and then called out in surprise, 'Surely it's Mr Hikobei!'

'And you are Otetsu!' the pedlar recognized her. 'In this downpour I didn't even realize where I was!'

'Come on in, don't stand there outside!' the maid said in a kindly voice and called to someone inside. 'It's Mr Hikobei, ma'am, the man from Osaka, you always buy your hair oil from.'

'Really?' Mrs Otome's voice answered. 'Let him in, it's a long time since he last stopped here.'

Hikobei took the pack off his back, took off his sandals and entered the modest room, where there was a pleasant smell of incense. All the households in Edo were burning incense then, as it absorbed the dampness and counteracted the unpleasant smell of mould.

Mrs Otome, who was a kind and dignified old lady, pointed to a square cushion of purple silk and bade her guest be seated.

Hikobei knelt, bowed politely and took his place.

'It's high time the rainy season was over. It seems never-ending this year,' she sighed. 'It makes me uneasy, as if there was something unpleasant in the air.'

'You mustn't let it affect you so, ma'am,' Otetsu said. She had been in the service of Otome for many years. 'You probably aren't used to it yet. After all we only came here from your nephew's house a year ago. It was different there, people about all the time, while here we live alone.'

'You are probably right,' Mrs Otome agreed. 'It is more peaceful here but sometimes I long for company. I suppose you feel the same way too, Hikobei?' the old lady turned to the visitor. 'I am always pleased to see you because we are something like fellow countrymen. I spent my youth in Osaka and am glad to hear someone speaking the dialect.'

'Yes, everybody in Edo can tell that I am not from here the moment I open my mouth. Some of my customers don't trust me because of that,' Hikobei complained.

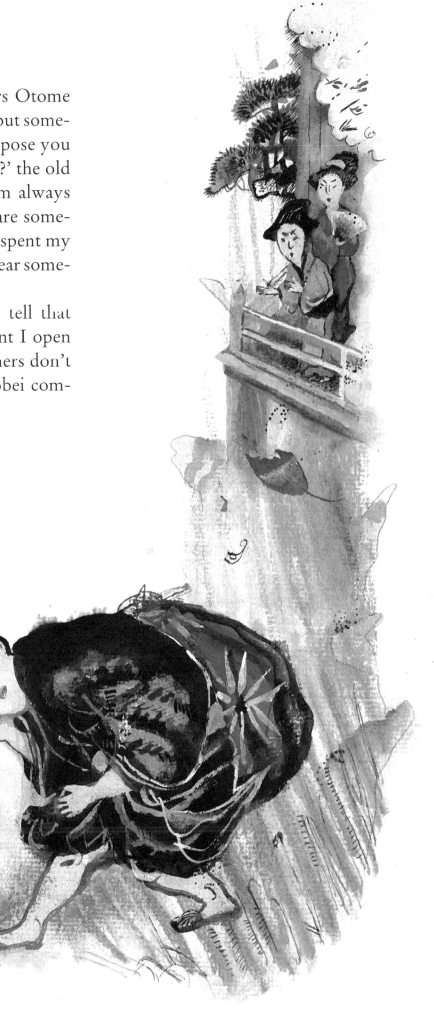

'They soon find out that you are a good, honest man, though, don't they, Otetsu,' the old lady turned to her servant. Otetsu nodded.

'If you should need anything, you know who to turn to,' Otome smiled affably.

'Yes, madam,' Hikobei again bowed low. 'Well, you know...' suddenly he looked embarrassed.

'Tell me what's troubling you,' Otome encouraged him.

'You have already helped me out once, when you lent me money, and you will remember that I paid it back on time.'

'Come to the point!'

'Since chance has brought me here, I wonder if I might ask you for a loan of one hundred ryo,' Hikobei cleared his throat. 'I should have been paid by a Ryogoku customer today but he wasn't at home. I need to buy some goods and to send money to my wife and children. The Feast of the Dead is drawing near.' Hikobei looked questioningly at the old lady.

'You say one hundred ryo,' she said thoughtfully. 'I happen to have it right here,' and she pointed to a brocade purse next to her. 'I have just been counting it. In my prayers to the Goddess of Mercy I promised to give it to her temple in the Low Grass Quarter. I must keep my promise, otherwise I would make her angry, though I know she is the kindest of all the gods and goddesses.'

'I would not dare to ask that of you. I know how devout you are and how everybody respects you for it. Forgive me for having mentioned it.'

'Wait, I have just realized I might be able to do something for you,' she called to her servant. 'Go to the back room and bring me the bamboo box from the chest, you know which one I mean. Put this money there to be safe for the night. I will take it to the abbot myself tomorrow

109

morning,' Otome said, holding out the pouch.

The servant obeyed and in a short while was back with an oblong box most ingeniously made of split bamboo, now dark with age.

The old lady took the box and slowly opened it. In it, on a silk pad the colour of wisteria flowers, lay a short dagger with an elegant handle inlaid with silver.

Hikobei looked at the valuable object with unconcealed admiration.

'Take the dagger,' Otome slowly pushed it towards him. 'You can get the sum you need if you pawn it. When you get your money from that customer, you can redeem it and bring it back to me. It is an unusual piece. It was given to me by my master at Osaka. That was a long time ago, when I was still very young and... oh, better not start reminiscing,' the old lady waved her hand.

'I don't know how to thank you,' Hikobei bowed several times. 'I promise to return it in a few days.'

'There's no hurry. As long as it helps you and your family,' Otome nodded her head. 'It has been lying useless in that chest for long enough.'

For a while the two went on talking about all sorts of things. Eventually it stopped raining and Hikobei said goodbye to the old lady and her servant. Putting his pack over his shoulder again he hurried home to the Lucky Well Quarter. It would be hard to say how this part of

the town came to have such a name. There was, in fact, more poverty than wealth to be seen there. Instead of spacious noble-men's houses there were long wooden *nagaya*, poor men's quarters, where whole families crowded into one small room.

While the servant Otetsu was preparing supper in the kitchen after Hikobei had left, she noticed a strange man peering through the back door. When she asked him what he wanted, he quickly disappeared. She noticed he limped a little.

She found it rather suspicious and told her mistress about it. The old lady sighed, saying, 'You can't trust anybody nowadays. We had better have our supper at once and go to bed early.'

No sooner had they eaten, when a messenger came running from her nephew's house with a message that he had guests and needed Otetsu to come and help him. She should stay at his house until the next morning.

'I don't know if I should leave my mistress alone at night,' Otetsu hesitated. 'She has been uneasy all day and added to that a suspicious character has been prowling around the house.'

'Go if they need you,' her mistress told her. 'I will lock the front and back doors well and nobody will get in.'

'Very well then,' the servant complied. 'I will hurry back in the morning to get here as soon as possible.'

Once Otetsu had left Otome put the padlock on both doors, climbed into bed and soon fell asleep.

It so happened that shortly before midnight two men, Gonza and Sukeju, whose job it was to carry people in sedan-chairs from one end of Edo to the other, went past the house. They had travelled a long way that day and could hardly stand on their feet. They had been as far as Azabu with a customer and still had quite a way to go to reach the Lucky Well Quarter, where they lived in the same *nagaya* as Hikobei. As they came closer to the house with their sedan-chair they noticed something flash like the blade of a sword under the porch roof. Then they heard water splashing in the tub under the gutter and saw somebody moving there. The unknown man who must have seen the lanterns on the sedan-chair disappeared into the darkness. The two men noticed that he limped slightly.

'That's strange!' Gonza whispered to his companion. 'Who could it be and what was he doing there? Let's go and look.'

They approached the house carefully. When they looked into the tub they noticed that the water was the colour of ripe peaches.

'Blood!' Sukeju cried out in alarm. 'That man must have killed somebody and was washing his sword here.'

'Be quiet!' Gonza hissed, and pulled his friend away by his arm.

Otetsu rose in the morning as soon as the sun came up and hurried home as she had promised her mistress. When she reached the house she was surprised to find the front door ajar.

'That's strange,' she thought. 'Madam is always so careful to see the doors are all locked.'

No sooner had she entered when she saw blood stains on the mats. Expecting the worst she flung open the door of her mistress's room. There she lay dead in a pool of blood.

'Murder, there's been a murder!' Otetsu screamed as if she were out of her mind and ran outside. Soon she was surrounded by a crowd of people and everybody had something to say about the dreadful affair. 'Such a good lady. She

never harmed a soul. Who could have done such a thing?'

Fortunately there was somebody sensible among them, who called the police.

The police soon arrived and looked around the premises with grave faces. 'Disperse! Nobody must enter the house! We need all the traces we can find!'

'Was it you that found the body? Who are you?' they asked Otetsu. Their chief told them to fetch the old lady's nephew Ichirozaemon, the owner of a rice shop. When he got over his shock he confirmed that the servant had spent the night at his house but that otherwise he knew nothing.

One of the policemen found the chest in the back chamber open. 'What is missing?' he asked the servant.

'I, I… don't…' Otetsu sobbed, scared.

'Speak up, you were the last person to see Mrs Otome alive.'

'There was one hundred ryo here and it is gone,' the servant at last managed to speak. 'My mistress wanted to take it herself to that abbot of the temple of the Goddness of Mercy today.'

'What else is missing?' the police wanted to know.

'I see that a valuable dagger in a bamboo case is missing, too,' the nephew noticed. 'My aunt showed it to me only quite recently.'

'My mistress gave it to Hikobei yesterday, to take it to a pawnshop,' Otetsu said.

'Who is Hikobei? What was he doing here? Why did Mrs Otome give him the dagger?' the policemen wanted to know.

They finally came to the conclusion that nobody else could be the murderer but Hikobei, for he knew the money had been there. They wouldn't listen to the servant who declared that he was innocent, that her mistress had known him over a year, and considered him a good and honest man. She was sure he would not do anything like that.

'Hold your tongue, or you'll come with us to the court in the South Town as a suspect!'

This frightened Otetsu so much that she didn't say another word.

The police chief ordered Hikobei to be arrested and brought before Judge Ooka.

News of the crime spread through Edo like fire in a wind. Before an hour had passed visitors to the public baths in the Lucky Well Quarter were already discussing it. A fat man said to his thin neighbour as they lay soaking in the hot water that morning, 'Have you heard about the murder in the Horse Through Quarter? They say that a hundred ryo are missing.'

'Not a hundred, it was a thousand!' the thin one insisted.

'No, no, they say it was only fifty!' a man whose body was tattooed from head to foot intervened.

'You are wrong, it was a thousand,' the thin one insisted. 'It happened in the family of the rice merchant! He's surely a rich man!'

'Isn't it better to be poor? No one would find anything to steal from us, would they?' the fat one laughed. 'You're right, though a few more copper or silver pieces would be welcome,' remarked the tattooed man, scratching his car.

'There's another murder, and they haven't found the scoundrel from Shiba yet,' a middle-aged man joined in. 'Who knows how much longer he'll be at large.'

At that moment Gonza and Sukeju emerged from the steam. 'There's nothing to beat the morning bath,' they agreed. 'It makes you feel reborn.'

'Oh, it's you!?' they recognized the men discussing the muder as their neighbours from the *nagaya*.

'You were late home last night! You must have been at the other end of the town again,' the tattooed one turned to them, for nothing remained secret in the *nagaya*.

'That's right. We carried a customer to Azabu!' Gonza replied.

'Then you may not have heard what happened last night in the Horse Trough Quarter.'

'What happened there?' Sukeju blurted out at once.

116

'Somebody did away with the rice merchant's aunt and ran off with a thousand ryo!'

'What?' Sukeju looked at Gonza and whispered in his ear, 'We were just passing…'

'All right, so what?' Gonza replied.

'Shouldn't we tell the police?'

'What are you two whispering about?' the tin man interrupted them. 'Are you the guilty party?'

'Mind your own business!' Gonza cut him short and nudged Sukeju. 'We have to go. We have a lot of work waiting for us today. So long!' The sedan-bearers said their farewells and left for another hard day's work.

When they came home in the early evening, there was great excitement outside the *nagaya*. Everybody was there, men, women, old, young and even children. The place was buzzing like a beehive. Women drew their heads close to hear one another better, men were waving their hands about in their excitement.

'What's going on?' the chair-bearers asked.

'Haven't you heard? They've come to arrest Hikobei,' somebody volunteered.

'Hikobei? What can he have done? Such a gentle and good man?' Gonza and Sukeju asked in amazement.

'They arrest him and let scoundrels run loose,' the wigmaker, known for her sharp tongue, exclaimed.

'Look, here they come,' said someone, pointing to the door of the *nagaya* as Hikobei came out with his hands bound, accompanied by policemen. He was very pale and his whole body was trembling. He stopped in front of the landlord and called out:

'Mr Rokurobei, I have never hurt a fly! Stand up for me, I beg you.'

'You can depend on me. I'll confirm you are a respectable man!' the landlord assured him.

'Thank you,' Hikobei bowed.

'Judge Ooka will set you free, when he finds out you are innocent,' people cried. 'Don't be afraid! We are with you!'

'That's enough,' the policemen inter-

fered. 'In the name of the Shogun, make way!'

There was nothing to be done but obey.

'Come back soon!' they called after Hikobei.

'If anything happens to me, don't forget to let my wife and children in Osaka know!' Hikobei turned to them for the last time.

'Don't worry!' the landlord assured him and took a few steps towards him. Needless to say the policeman stopped him, saying, 'You stay here. If you are needed we will call for you.'

'Very well, but if this man is guilty of a crime then the sun must have started to rise in the west instead of the east.'

Ten days passed and the people of the *nagaya* had heard no news of Hikobei. Among those inquiring about him was a young good-for-nothing Kantaro, who lived a few houses away and had several times shown up at the *nagaya*. Nobody knew what he did for a living. He said he sold fruit but instead of baskets on

a shoulder pole he was more often to be seen with his hands tucked in the wide sleeves of his kimono, lounging around Edo and looking for something to free or something to pinch. That was why the people didn't like seeing him round the *nagaya*.

The day the landlord was called to court to give evidence about Hikobei, Kantaro appeared unexpectedly in the Happy Well Quarter. He brought wine and sweet cakes, inviting everybody to join him.

'Where did you get the money to buy all this?' people asked.

'Why bother to ask?' Kantaro sneered. 'I won it in a lottery.'

'Such a good-for-nothing, and look at his luck,' people said behind his back but nobody refused the food and wine he offered. A chance like that to get something free did not come by every day.

Towards evening the landlord at last returned from court. It was evident at first sight that he was not bringing good news.

'Things look bad for Hikobei,' he told them. 'Everything seems to be against him. He was the last to see the money. Apart from the maid and the nephew, nobody else knew about it. The valuable dagger that had been in the chest in the back chamber was found in his room. The maid insists that Mrs Otome gave it to him to take to the pawnshop, but she is suspected of being his accomplice.'

'It must be true,' Kantaro said. 'After all he is being tried by Ooka and it is said in Edo that he is never wrong.'

'You can talk!' somebody snapped at him. 'Has Hikobei ever done you any harm?'

'No, but I wouldn't trust anyone from Osaka. Well, I'm off!' he said suddenly as if he had heard all he needed, and went home. By chance, Gonza and Sukeju were just returning and saw the young man leaving. Sukeju nudged his friend: 'Look, he has the same walk as the man

we saw that night in the Horse Trough Quarter. He's limping!' Sukeju said, nudging his friend. 'You are right, I thought the same,' Gonze agreed. They said no more as the wigmaker came to tell them that nothing could help Hikobei.

'That's terrible!' the sedan-bearers were dismayed. 'He is certainly innocent!'

'Ask the landlord, he'll tell you,' the woman pointed to Rokurobei, who was standing nearby.

'She is right,' he sighed. 'Now I will have to write to his wife and children in Osaka.'

'I wouldn't care to be in their situation,' a women sighed and covered her eyes with her sleeves, so no-one could see that they were full of tears.

When the landlord had gone, Sukeju whispered to Gonza:

'Don't you think we should tell the police what we saw? We may be able to save him.'

'You're crazy. I tell you they'd suspect us if we did!' Gonza snapped at him.

'Don't forget he is being tried by Ooka, and he is a fair and just judge.'

'You know how justice works!' Gonza replied.

Now, let us go to Osaka, days and weeks away from Edo on foot. However, letters were delivered by fast messengers on horseback, changing mounts several times on the way, and it did not take long before Hikobei's wife heard that her husband had been sentenced to death.

'That can't be true!' she wept and called her two sons to tell them the distressing news.

'Although it's here in black and white, it's a lie. Your father is innocent. He was always a good and honest man.'

'We can't leave it like that, mother!' said the older of the two, Hikisaburo, who was just fifteen. 'I will go to Edo and do my utmost to clear his name.'

'Do you know, my boy, what a long journey it is, and what can await you?'

'Nothing can be too hard if it helps my father. I will be glad to go and am not afraid of anything,' Hikisaburo said bravely.

'Go, then. It is the right thing for a son to do,' his mother encouraged him, and went to tie some food in a bundle for him to take on his way and to get him a pilgrim's staff and straw sandals. She put a few coppers into a purse at his belt in case of need.

'I wish you a safe journey and may you succeed,' she said, embracing him with tears in her eyes.

The boy set out on the dusty road winding along the Eastern Sea called Tokaido, which linked the capital Kyoto and hereby Osaka with Edo. He walked on tirelessly by day and by night, enduring the scorching sun, the rain and the cold, and in two months he reached Edo, passing by Suzukamori, where the notorious prison and the execution ground were. It was a very dark night and there was a ghastly smell in the air. Hikisaburo was terrified and wanted to run away as fast as he could, when he saw two lanterns coming towards him along the road. Gonza and Sukeju were returning home with their sedan. The boy hid behind a tree not to be seen. The sedan-bearers stopped a few feet away from him.

'Let's have a little rest,' said Gonza putting down the sedan.

'You're right, it's been a hard day today. Such a long distance and that fat customer seemed to get heavier and heavier. It would have done him good to change places with us for at least part of the way,' Sukejo sighed.

'No help for it! We have to earn our living!' Gonza answered.

'Whenever we come past this awful place I think of Hikobei,' Sukeju spoke up again. 'He was punished for a crime somebody else had committed. After all, we saw that lame man washing his blood-stained sword in the tub under the roof gutter. We should have told the police!'

'What's done is done. That's how it is in life. There's no justice for the poor. Come on, it's getting cold!' and Gonza bent to lift the sedan.

At first Hikisaburo was not listening, but when he heard his father's name he made sure not to miss a word of what they were saying. When they set out again he followed them. Gonza and Sukeju were fast walkers and the boy sometimes despaired of keeping the light of their lanterns in sight along the winding road. Fortunately he always managed to catch up with them but it all seemed like a bad dream from which he must soon wake up.

When it was nearly daybreak the sedan-bearers reached the Happy Well Quarter and turned into the street where the *nagaya* stood.

One was called Gonza, the boy thought, I heard the other one calling him that. I must remember the name to find him tomorrow. He lay down by a timber and was soon dead to the world.

Early next morning the *nagaya* was lively. It was just before the feast of the autumn equinox and led by the landlord the tenants were cleaning their rooms. Pata, pata, don, don, the clattering of brooms and dusting brushes could be heard.

'You see how well it goes,' the landlord praised them. 'In a short while everything will be spick and span. There is nothing to beat a good clean-out.'

Just then Hikisaburo appeared. Sukeju was carrying a mattress out of the house. 'Can't you get out of the way, you clumsy fool,' the bearer shouted at Hikisaburo. When he looked at the boy again, he said less harshly, 'I can see you are a pilgrim. Where have you come from and who are you looking for?'

'I am looking for Mr Rokurobei. I got a letter from him and have come all the way from Osaka.'

'Aren't you Hikobei's son?'

'Yes, my name is Hikisaburo.'

Sukeju called the landlord at once.

'Welcome, my boy,' Rokurobei said to him in a kind voice. 'You have travelled a long way. Would you like to rest a while?'

'No, I haven't come to rest,' Hikisaburo answered. 'I am here to clear my father's name.'

'You are a dutiful son, but I don't know how you will be able to do that,' the landlord hesitated. 'They say your father confessed. He was tried by Ooka, who is known never to make mistakes.'

'Even the best judge can make a mistake,' the boy insisted. 'I know my father can't be brought back to life but his name must be cleared. I have proof of his innocence.'

'Indeed, what proof?' the landlord asked in surprise and everybody stopped talking.

'Is there a sedan-bearer called Gonza living in the *nagaya*?'

'Yes, that's him over there,' the landlord pointed in the direction of the well. 'Sukeju is by him, they work together. Where do you know Gonza from?'

'I don't know him but by chance I overheard what they were talking about last night near the prison at Suzukamori.'

'And what were they saying?' the people drew nearer to the boy.

'That they know the real culprit.'

'How is that possible? Why didn't they say so at the trial?' everybody exclaimed.

'Come here,' the landlord bade the two bearers, who complied unwillingly.

'Now tell us truthfully what you know about this business,' Rukorobei ordered them sternly.

'Oh, nothing, that's just gossip. Hikisaburo must have mistaken us for somebody else,' the two said evasively.

'I heard them, I swear I did,' the boy interrupted them. 'They were saying that they saw the murderer that night, washing his sword in the tub under the roof gutter.'

'Gonza, Sukeju, that's enough!' said the landlord irately. 'Out with the truth!'

'Aren't you sorry for the boy!' the people were angry.

'Let Gonza begin,' Sukeju nudged his friend.

'Why should I? You start!'

At that a young woman with a child on her back pushed forward. 'You just listen to me, Gonza,' she planted herself in front of him and looked him straight in the face. 'If you know something then say it here in front of everybody and show you are a man and not a coward!'

'If that's what you think,' Gonza fidgeted, suddenly meek face to face with his own wife. 'But what if Sukeju…'

'I said you should start!'

'How did it really happen?' the landlord interrupted the marital argument.

'It was a hot and damp summer night. We were returning from Azabu and…'

'It was just midnight,' Sukeju continued as Gonza paused, wanting to share the limelight, when he saw that everyone was listening. 'We were passing through the Horse Trough Quarter when suddenly we saw…'

'What did you see?' somebody asked.

'Let Gonza finish,' Sukeju said, losing his courage at the crucial moment.

'We saw somebody washing a sword in the tub under the roof gutter of Mrs Otome's house. When he noticed the light of our lanterns he ran away.'

'Who was it?' asked the landlord.

'How can we know? It was night, wasn't it Sukeju?' Gonza turned to his comrade.

'But, we did notice, that he limped,' burst out Sukeju, 'so it must have been…'

'Kantaro,' Gonza at last came out with the truth.

'We must go and tell the police,' the landlord decided.

'No, no,' the two sedan-bearers protested. 'We don't want to have anything to do with the police.'

'You have my word no harm will come to you! But I'd better tie you up to make sure you don't run away before we get there. Bring some strong rope,' the landlord ordered.

In a short while the strange procession started off for the South Town led by Mr Rokurobei, followed by Hikisaburo and the two bearers, bound so tightly they could hardly breathe.

There Ooka just questioned the boy, then Gonza and Sukeju, and having heard what they had to say, he sent for Kantaro.

When they brought him in, Ooka asked him, 'Tell us what happened that July night in the quarter of the Horse Trough?'

'Why should anything have happened? I don't know of anything! What am I here for?' Kantaro protested impudently.

'You are here because there's something important I want to ask you about,' Ooka told him.

'I haven't done anything! Let me go! You have no proof!' Kantaro cried.

Ooka took no notice of this improper outburst and said, 'I will give you time to think about it. The court is adjourned.'

The judge took advantage of the interval to hear the result of the search he had ordered carried out where Kantaro lived.

Ooka began the afternoon court hearing with the question: 'What do you do for a living, Kantaro?'

'I sell fruit. Peaches at the end of spring, melons in summer, in autumn pears and apples, in winter persimmons.'

'Then why were there no fruit baskets found in your place?'

'Baskets? In my place?'

'Instead we discovered this!'

At a sign from Ooka the court official held up a cotton kimono with a blood-stained sleeve.

'What does this mean? Have you any explanation?' Ooka demanded.

'Yes, of course,' Kantaro quickly recovered. 'One night a dog was howling dreadfully in our quarter. I couldn't sleep and so I took a stick and battered its head.'

'Why then did you hide the kimono under a mat where the police found it?'

That at last made Kantaro hesitate. He tried to resist for a short while longer but in the end confessed to everything.

When they led him away, Ooka turned to Hikisaburo saying, 'Now your father's name has been cleared. Are you satisfied?'

The boy wept bitterly. 'What use is it to me, Your Honour,' he said when he had calmed down a little. 'He was sentenced to death though he was innocent. Nobody can bring him back to life.'

'The boy is right!' Gonza said, suddenly becoming bold.

'Yes, it only shows that even Judge Ooka can make a mistake!' Sukeju supported him. The two bearers looked at each other, surprised at their audacity.

'Quiet, please!' said Ooka, raising his voice and nodding at his assistent. 'Let the prisoner who was brought here from Suzukamori appear.'

'Who can that be?' the unvoiced question hung in the air. Everybody was waiting in tense silence, to see who it would be.

At last the door opened and the guards brought in a thin, middle-aged man, whose pale face reflected the suffering he had been through.

'Do you recognize him?' Ooka turned to Hikisaburo.

'Father!' the boy ran to the prisoner and embraced him.

'What are you doing here, son?' asked Hikobei, as if he did not believe his eyes.

'I came here for you, or rather I thought that you...'

'As you see, your father is alive,' Ooka intervened. 'And he will be set free this very day.'

'What has happened?' the boy asked the judge, in disbelief.

'I will tell you,' Ooka smiled. 'When I was investigating Hikobei I became convinced that a man like him could never have committed such a crime. However, I didn't have enough proof to allow me to set him free. That's why I announced that he would be sentenced to death, but I did not actually pass sentence, as everybody assumed. I waited to see if some chance would help me to solve the case. Today it finally happened. If Gonza and Sukeju had come to me sooner with their testimony, Hikobei and his family would have been spared great suffering.'

The two sedan-bearers could hardly look anyone in the face, they were so ashamed.

'And we even dared to doubt your judgement!' they cried, banging the floor with their foreheads as they bowed.

127

'Let this be a lesson to you in the future,' Ooka said without anger. 'It is true you had little faith but you have given great help in catching the true culprit. You can both claim a reward of ten ryo.'

After that Ooka made a sign to his assistant: 'This was the last case, and it has been solved. There are others waiting for us. It is high time we started to work on them.'

The Trussed Statue

DURING the time when Ooka was a judge in Edo, there was a poor young fellow called Yagoro living in the Treasure Quarter, Takaracho. He was an honest and hard working man such as were hard to come by. His master, Hachigoemon, the owner of a silk shop, trusted him completely and sent him on errands he would not have entrusted to anyone else.

One day Hachigoemon sent Yagoro to a customer at the other end of the town with some bolts of white silk. Yagoro wrapped them in a blue cloth bearing his master's name and threw the pack on his back, lifting it a little so it would sit comfortably. It was quite heavy but Yagoro was used to carrying such loads.

'Don't stop anywhere and come back quickly,' his master called after him as he was leaving the house. 'I will need you in the shop.'

Yagoro nodded and bowing respectfully set off. It was a fresh morning of a beautiful summer day but Yagoro had no time to look about him. He was walking so fast that his sandals flapped against his heels. He slowed down only as he was passing the flower market to look at the morning glories. In Japan these flowers are called 'morning cheeks' because they open at daybreak. If you want to admire them, you must rise early in the morning. The gardeners had flowerpots standing

all around them. There were so many colours that it was dazzling. No wonder that
people found it hard to choose, going

from one stand to another before deciding which plant to buy. Yagoro could not resist them either and stopped for a moment to look at the morning glory covered with pink blossoms, which attracted him most, but remembering his master's words, he soon quickened his pace to make up for the short delay.

He still had a long way to go. As he went the sun grew hotter and hotter until Yagoro was dripping with sweat. He kept wiping his face with a white cloth which he had tucked into the sash of his garment. The silk on his back got heavier and heavier as if it were a bag of stones, and he had to keep shifting it to make it easier to carry. He stopped at a tea stall because he had become very thirsty. Drinking his tea standing up he immediately hurried on his way. It was nearly noon. The heat was oppressive and Yagoro was getting very tired. Suddenly he saw a tree standing by the road and next to it a statue of the God Jizo, the patron of children and pilgrims. This statue can be found on all Japanese roads, usually surrounded by children at play. Poor Jizo is often quite knocked about by them. Now, however, it was just noon and the little mischiefs had gone home. It was peaceful there and the cool shade of the tree was irresistible.

Yagoro took the pack off his back and laid it on the ground before the statue. He lay down in the grass a few steps away. What bliss this was, especially at moments when a slight breeze sprang up. Before long Yagoro's eyes began to close and soon he was asleep. He dreamed about the morning glory in bloom and it was a lovely dream.

Suddenly, still half asleep, he heard a rough voice say, 'Well, that's that!' He was up in a moment and dashed to the statue of Jizo in front of which he had left the silk. The statue was still standing there and the saint was still looking down on the world with the same kind, slightly surprised look on his stone face, but the pack of silk was nowhere to be seen. Instead, on the spot where it had lain, there was only dusty and trampled grass.

My sight must be failing me in this heat, Yagoro thought in dismay. He looked around once more, even searching the bushes nearby, but the bundle of silk had disappeared, as if had been swallowed up by the earth.

Whatever will I do? What will my master say? To have the goods he entrusted me stolen from under my very nose! He reminded me to go straight there and not to delay anywhere, Yagoro lamented silently and stood helplessly on the road.

In a flash of inspiration he thought: I must go to the court. There they will advise me what to do. Without more ado he ran to the South Town, where he found Ooka. The judge was just resting and fanning himself. Yagoro, quite out of breath, recounted what had happened to him. The judge listened carefully and then turned to the court assistants and ordered them to bind the statue immediately and bring it to court.

His assistants looked at him in surprise; not one of them moved to do his bidding. 'But it's a stone statue, Your Honour,' one of them dared to protest. 'What use would it be to you?'

'You are the oldest here and you ought

to know that my orders should be carried out at once and without question,' Ooka rebuked him. 'However, as you have asked, I will tell you why I want the statue brought here. Jizo is not only the protector of children but also of pilgrims. If he allowed a pack left under his protection to be stolen, then he has betrayed Yagoro's trust and must be brought to trial the same as everybody else. What kind of justice would it be otherwise?'

Without another word the assistants took ropes and a prison cart with them and went to Meguro where the theft had taken place.

They soon found the poor Jizo, who was to be brought to trial for neglecting his duties. They rolled up their sleeves, brought out the rope and started winding it around the statue until only the head showed. It needed all their efforts to get the stone Jizo on to the cart. By this time quite a crowd of people from the neighbourhood had gathered to watch them.

They wanted to know what was going to happen to their Jizo but the court assistants did not waste much time on them. 'We're taking him to the judge,' they said indifferently. 'Now, stop hanging about and get out of the way!' As the cart passed through the streets of Edo the crowd following them increased.

'Where are they taking it?' asked the late comers.

'They are taking it to court.'

'Why is it trussed up like that?'

'It's committed a crime. It is to be tried.'

'You're talking nonsence! A stone statue can't speak!'

'Ooka will teach it to speak, don't you worry,' somebody called out. Everyone laughed and crowded after the cart into the court.

There were all in such high spirits that they did not notice Ooka, who had entered and taken his place accompanied by his guards. When the noise did not stop, he called out loudly, 'Silence! What is going on here? Who do you think you are to burst in here in that way and disturb the peace of the supreme court for no reason at all? That is an inexcusable offence. Every one of you will pay a fine of three gold pieces, as punishment.'

The people could not believe their ears. A fine of three gold pieces! Where would they get so much money from? They were only poor people, after all, craftsmen, pedlars and messengers, who lived from one day to the next. Ooka knew very well how inquisitive the people of Edo were and if there was anything happening they had to be on the spot. It was one of the few pleasures life offered them. Now they were going to have to pay a fine for it, and a heavy one at that!

'How can we pay three gold pieces?' voices were raised in protest.

Ooka waited a little while and then spoke again, his voice sounding less official: 'I know you came here out of curiosity and not with evil intentions. I am not surprised you thought it strange when you saw what was taking place at Meguro. A stone statue has certainly never testified at court before. However, I am convinced Jizo will wish to put things right and will help us catch the thief.'

'Who stole what?' people asked.

'Don't worry about that now,' Ooka cut them short. 'Firstly we must settle this matter. I will reduce your fines from three gold pieces to a piece of white silk one inch wide and two inches long. I give you an hour in which to bring it here, wherever you have to get it from, but first the scribe will take down your names and addresses, in case any of you should change his mind.'

How relieved they all were! A bit of white silk is easier to find at home than three gold pieces. The clerks noted down the names and addresses of everyone present before letting them go.

Before long people began coming back with bits of white silk. Ooka and Yagoro stood beneath the trussed statue inspecting the pieces one by one.

Suddenly Yagoro whispered to Ooka in excitement: 'That's it! That is it for sure!' Already a guard was holding the man who had brought that piece of silk and was trying to disappear quickly. How could he have guessed he would give himself away like that. He had only been curious how a stone statue would testify and now he was going to have to pay for it dearly.

'Free the statue!' Ooka ordered. 'It has made good its offence by helping to catch the thief.'

From that time on it became the custom in Edo to report all unsolved thefts to the stone Jizo at Meguro and to truss it up with rope until the thief was caught. Since there are so many dishonest people, taking what does not belong to them, and more of them instead of fewer, as time goes on, Jizo is tied up with ropes all the time and now is called the Trussed Statue. It stands at Meguro to this day, and if you don't believe me, go and look!

The Dispute Between the Barber
and the Woodcutter

TODAY I am going to tell you how Ooka settled the dispute between Sakubei, the barber, and Kyutaro, the woodcutter.

First I must reveal that Sakubei liked to play jokes on people and he was well-known for it in the whole neighbourhood. Nothing gave him more pleasure than to make a fool of the good-natured villagers who came to Edo to earn some money.

One day Kyutaro, the woodcutter, passed Sakubei's shop with his cart harnessed to an ox. He was going home from the market where he went from time to time to sell some wood. This time he had

done well and was returning home contented. Sakubei was standing outside his shop and Kyutaro's honest, guileless face gave him an idea: he could make a fool of him and make a profit at the same time. As he never thought twice about anything, he called to the woodcutter, 'Hullo, there! Wait, I want to make a bargain with you!'

Kyutaro pulled the reins and jumped down from the cart.

'What do you want?' he asked.

'When you next come to town, stop here on the way. I will buy the cart full of wood from you for ten coppers and in addition will shave you and your assistant,' said the barber, pointing to the young man in the driver's seat.

Sakubei expected the woodcutter to argue about the price and want a copper or two more, but the countryman just stroked the stubble on his chin and said, 'Good, that'll be very convenient.'

'Agreed then,' Sakubei replied, pleased with himself. 'Don't put it off too long. I haven't got anything to make a fire with.'

Kyutaro only nodded. From childhood he had always lived in a solitary hut in the woods and was not in the habit of holding long conversations with town dwellers. He kept his word and a few days later brought the cart piled high with well-dried wood. The barber came running out of his shop and without a word paid him ten copper coins.

'Where shall I pile the wood?' Kyutaro asked.

'Why do that?' the barber pretended to be surprised. 'Leave it here as it is. Just unharness your ox and take him with you.'

'What do you mean?' the woodcutter was puzzled. 'After all, I must unload the wood first, so I can drive the cart away.'

'That would be too simple,' the barber shook his head. 'We agreed that I would buy the cart full of wood. You did not have any objections, did you?'

'Yes, but...'

'There you are! There is no but. The cart and the wood belong to me and that's that. Just let me shave you and you can go about your business.'

'You can't be serious, Mr Sakubei,' the woodcutter protested weakly.

'Then I will put you right. I'm deadly serious. Now hurry up. Where would I be, if I wasted time with every village blockhead like you?'

'What will I do without a cart?' the woodcutter lamented. 'I'll never save enough to buy a new one. My whole family depends on it. It can't be of any use to you, Mr Sakubei, anyway.'

'That's no business of yours. Just do what I have told you to.'

'This can't be possible, good people,' said the woodcutter, turning for help to the barber's customers, who had witnessed the whole dispute. 'Tell him so!'

The one whose turn it was to be shaved only laughed amused, and was unwilling to intervene. The next one was evidently sorry for the woodcutter.

'What good is a cart to you, Sakubei? Will you use it to drive lather about?' he tried to turn the whole affair into a joke. 'And Kyutaro, here, can't do without it. You ought to be ashamed of yourself.'

Another customer, a chubby, well-dressed man joined in: 'Why shouldn't Sakubei keep the cart? In my opinion it's his. A cart full of wood is a cart full of wood. One must know how to do business, or else keep out of it.'

'You can't do that! You'd have the skin off our backs,' a skinny man protested unable to keep silent. He held a child by the hand, and it started to cry, frightened.

'What's going on here?' suddenly policemen's voices called out from behind them.

'Get along with your cart, you're in the way here,' one of them told the woodcutter roughly.

'Sakubei here refuses to let me take it away,' the woodcutter protested.

'Who says I refuse!' Sakubei shouted loudly. 'It is his fault, he refuses to stick to our bargain. The cart is mine!'

'I'm not going to argue about that with you,' the chief of the police stopped him. 'If you can't come to some agreement, go to the judge.'

'Why not?' the barber agreed at once. 'Collect your bits and pieces and let's go,' he told the frightened woodcutter.

Kyutaro trembled at the very thought of going to court but he did not dare to refuse.

Sakubei sent all his customers home and locked the shop. When they finally reached the court with the cart, the barber went in confidently, as if he owned the place, for he was sometimes sent for to shave the clerks and attendants. Kyutaro looked shyly around. He had never been to court and was fearful of everything there. He was just going to pluck the barber's sleeve and tell him he could keep the cart, when someone at his side whispered, 'Don't be afraid. If you are in the right Ooka will not harm you.'

Kyutaro looked gratefully at the stranger. His advice gave him courage to go through with the case against the barber.

'What brings you here?' Ooka asked when he saw the strange couple, one a weather-beaten countryman, the other a spotlessly clean barber.

'Your Honour, this clodhopper from who knows where has the cheek to try and cheat me, a citizen of the ancient town of Edo,' the barber pointed at the woodcutter.

'What is he cheating you of?' Ooka wanted to know.

'A cart, my lord,' the barber hastened to reply. 'Allow me to tell you everything from the beginning.' He took a deep breath and started off. 'When Kyutaro passed my shop a few days ago, I offered to buy from him a cart full of wood for ten coppers and to shave him and his assistant too, and he agreed.'

'I can see that you haven't shaved him yet,' Ooka remarked dryly.

The woodcutter bent his head in shame as if the judge were reprimanding him.

'How could I?' the barber said unper-

turbed. 'I have been arguing with him about the cart half the day. He refuses to let me have it although it was agreed. I told him quite clearly that I would buy a cart full of wood. It stands to reason I wouldn't offer him ten coppers for a few rotten pieces of wood. He claims only the wood is mine, without the cart!'

'What would I use to take wood to town in,' Kyutaro blurted out, forgetting to address the judge properly as any well-behaved person would have done. 'I have eight children, a wife and an old mother to feed.'

'That has nothing to do with the case,' Ooka stopped him. 'An agreement has to be respected. Where would we be if everyone did just what he felt like. Now, let me clarify this again. You, barber Sakubei, ordered a cart full of wood from this woodcutter Kyutaro. You promised to pay him ten copper coins for it and shave him and his assistant. Is that right?'

'Yes, exactly,' the barber confirmed eagerly.

'Yes, that is true,' Kyutaro nodded, because there was nothing else he could do.

'Did you pay him, Sakubei?' the judge asked.

'As soon as he brought the wood, Your Honour. I,' the barber emphasized, 'pay my bills and keep my promises, not like some people.' As he said this the barber looked at the woodcutter accusingly.

'Did you get ten copper coins from Sakubei for the cart full of wood?' Ooka turned to the woodcutter.

'Yes, I've got them here,' said Kyutaro touching his sash.

'Then the first condition of your agreement has been fulfilled,' Ooka conclu-

ded this part of the investigation. 'However, you still have to shave Kyutaro and his assistant.'

'I'll be glad to do so,' the barber bowed obligingly, as if his best customer were standing before him. 'I can do it here on the spot. Come nearer, Kyutaro.'

'Kyutaro can remain unshaven a short time longer,' Ooka interrupted. 'First shave his assistant.'

'Unfortunately, I cannot do that, although I would be glad to comply. You see, Kyutaro came without an assistant today,' the barber declared triumphantly.

'Who helped him to pull the cart?' Ooka asked innocently.

'The ox, Your Honour, that stands to reason,' said the barber, shaking his head at Ooka's question.

'Don't be so surprised,' the judge admonished him. 'The ox is Kyutaro's assistant today. When you have shaved him then you will have only Kyutaro to shave before the cart, as well as the wood, is yours. But not before you have done so,' said Ooka firmly.

'Shave an ox? I've never heard of such a thing in my life, Your Honour,' the barber protested, much less confidently than before.

'I have never heard of anybody buying wood and keeping the cart, either,' replied Ooka sharply. 'However, if you don't want to lose the case, then do what I have told you. Shave the ox in the courtyard so everybody can see it and judge your work.'

Sakubei did not dare to oppose him. He was obliged to send his apprentice for his shaving tackle and to rack his brains about how to shave an ox.

News of what was about to happen spread through the town in no time and people came rushing to the courtyard to watch.

Meanwhile Kyutaro unharnessed the ox, patting it goodnaturedly on the head, as if to prepare it for what was going to happen.

In no time the apprentice was back with the razor and other things. Sakubei was quite himself again, looking self-confident and trying to give the impression that an ox was a customer like any other. He put some warm water in the bowl, took the shaving brush in his hand and was ready to start. No sooner had he raised his hand to lather the beast's muzzle when it snorted angrily and taking the poor barber up with its horns, flung him to the ground. The barber did not give up so easily. He jumped up quickly, collected his tackle and tried again but with what result! The ox flung him into the biggest puddle the rain had left the previous night. It was a sight to make you laugh your head off. The whole court was in an uproar and all the windows were full of people watching. Nobody wanted to miss such entertainment. When they saw what the ox was doing with the barber they could have split their sides with laughter.

Sakubei tried it twice more but each time the ox gave him such a rough time that he finally gave up. Ordering his apprentice to collect his tackle, which was scattered all over the yard, he limped to Ooka.

'Well, have you fulfilled the terms of the agreement and shaved the assistant?' the judge asked him gravely, although at the sight of the dismal Sakubei his lips were twitching with a suppressed smile.

'Your Honour, he wouldn't let me,' Sakubei answered faintly, holding a large bruise on his cheek.

'Don't you want to try again?' Ooka asked. 'We have plenty of time. I would not have it said that there is not justice at my court.'

'Not on your life, Your Honour. The beast,' Sakubei caught himself up, 'I mean, that cursed assistant of Kyutaro's has nearly been the death of me. I never want to see him again.'

'You have got what you asked for.

145

Next time, I hope you will be more careful before playing your tricks and will think twice before cheating such a good and honest man such as Kyutaro. In compensation you must at least, shave him.'

'I would be glad to, Your Honour, but I am in such a state that I can hardly move and my hands are shaking.'

'Then pay him and he can go to another barber!'

That was the last straw for Sakubei's conceit. But what else could he do? Unwillingly he paid Kyutaro, who added the money to the ten coppers he had received for the wood. Thanking Ooka, he set off with his cart.

A Charm to Cure Forgetfulness

DURING Ooka's time as judge, there lived a woman called Chiko with her husband at Shinagawa, a village on the shore of a bay near Edo.

They had a few fields and although fate did not bless them with children, they were happy and contented. One day, however, the man fell ill and before long it was evident that there was no help for him. He found it hard to leave his wife alone and with no-one to support her.

After he died Chiko was so desolate that for some time she was like a lost soul. When she recovered a little she saw that the rice fields she had tended with her husband for so long were overgrown with weeds and that the whole place was going to rack and ruin because it was too much for her.

Chiko decided to sell everything and buy a small shop in the town with the money. Before long she found a buyer who was ready to pay five hundred gold pieces for the house and fields. The widow consented and they soon reached an agreement.

Chiko found it hard to leave the house but there was nothing else she could do. To have a souvenir of better days she took with her a portable brazier, a *hibachi,* on which she and her husband used to make tea. They had bought it soon after their wedding. It was a beautiful one with flowers inlaid with mother-of-pearl on the outer wall that gleamed with all the colours of the rainbow and looked real. As she carried the *hibachi* away she wept over her fate. There was no help for it. She had to get used to being quite alone. She rented a small room near the Nihon-bashi Bridge and looked forward to working in the small shop she would buy, where time would pass more quickly.

One morning, when it was just autumn and the days were peaceful and bright, Chiko put on her best kimono, took with her the five hundred gold pieces and went to visit the moneylender Chogoro, who lived nearby. She wanted to ask his advice about putting her money to good use. Chiko was new in the town and she had no idea that Chogoro was known far and wide as a cunning old fox who made money on everything he did, wringing the last penny from every client even if it killed them. In fact, where money was concerned, Chogoro had no mercy for anyone.

When he saw Chiko his eyes sparkled like a predator's at the sight of helpless prey. He rubbed his hands with glee, welcoming the widow with such sweet words that never a doubt crossed her mind.

One word led to another and before much time had passed Chiko had entrusted Chogoro with all her money. The moneylender made great promises of what a profitable business he would find for her, assuring her that she had no need to worry and that she had placed her money in the right hands.

'You must be patient though,' he said. 'It may take a while, but the moment I find something suitable I will let you know.'

The widow felt quite dizzy from everything he had told her and so it is no wonder she forgot to ask him to give her a receipt for her money.

She came home feeling satisfied and was glad she would soon have a place to call her own. Now there was nothing to do but wait until Chogoro sent her a message. The days passed, autumn was gone, then winter and already the first plum trees were beginning to bloom. Chiko decided she would wait no longer. Again she put on her best clothes and went to visit Chogoro. This time Chogoro did not welcome her with sweet words nor did he show any politeness. He pretended he did not know her.

'But I am Chiko, the widow who placed five hundred gold pieces with you in the middle of the ninth month of last year,' she reminded him.

'You must be mad, woman,' the moneylender said harshly. 'I have never seen you before in my life nor have I ever had any money from you. You must be out of your mind.'

'You must remember me, Mr Chogoro,' the widow protested. 'You promised you would find a small shop for my money and that you would tell me as soon as you had found one.'

'All right then,' said Chogoro nodding his head. 'One of us must be speaking the truth and one of us is lying. That's quite clear. Show me your receipt!'

The widow was aghast. She did not have a receipt. 'You didn't give me one,' she managed to say.

'Go and tell that to somebody else, not me,' Chogoro laughed scornfully. 'Would you trust anybody with so much money without wanting a receipt? Only a fool would do such a thing.'

'I thought...' the widow started to cry.

'Don't cry now,' Chogoro said in a conciliatory tone. 'When I have a little time I will go through my records and send for you.'

The widow became calmer. She went home and waited five days, then another five but no news came from the moneylender, so she went to visit him once more. This time Chogoro did not even answer her greeting properly and pretended to be deeply engrossed in his work.

'Oh, it's you,' he said at last, when he deigned to lift his eyes from his account books. 'I have lost several days because of you. I've looked through all my records and checked every single item, but there is no mention of your money.'

'Mr Chogoro, that's impossible. You must have missed it. Please have another look,' the desperate widow begged him.

'Now I've really had enough,' the moneylender made a show of anger. 'I am an honest man and have the best reputation among my customers. I tell you I have no money of yours!'

'That money is all I have,' the widow lamented. 'I am quite alone in the world. What am I going to live on in my old age?'

'That's none of my business. Get out and stay out. I don't want to set eyes on you here again,' Chogoro shouted at her.

When the widow showed no signs of leaving, he called for his servants and ordered them to show her out of his house.

Chiko finally realized that the moneylender was a crook out to cheat her of all her money. She determined not to give up, and the next day she came to his house again. She found the door locked and knocked in vain.

That night Chiko was so sad and worried she could not go to sleep. What was she to do, now that Chogoro had left her without any resources? What else could she do but find work? She was no longer young and so in the end she was glad to find job as a servant to a rich family. Hard times set in. She worked from morning until night without a kind word from anyone. And she hated Chogoro so fiercely that she could hardly eat or sleep. In the end she fell ill and lost her job.

From then on she lived from hand to mouth, doing odd jobs; she grew weaker day by day.

In the meantime Chogoro prospered. The poor widow remembered the old saying that evil people sleep well, and thought how true it was.

When another ten years of misery had passed Chiko no longer wanted to go on living, and decided she would revenge herself on Chogoro whatever the cost.

One day as she sat looking at her only reminder of better times, the brazier with its mother-of-pearl flowers, she decided to set fire to the Chogoro's house. As soon as darkness fell, she blew on the charcoal in the *hibachi*. It burned so brightly that she needed no lantern to light her way. She crept cautiously into Chogoro's garden through the back gate and went towards the wooden verandah where she meant to scatter the burning embers. At the last moment she hesitated. After all Chogoro had an old mother and children, she thought, and they could burn to death. As she stood here undecided, she heard a sound close by. Her blood turned cold. Somebody's coming, she thought, and fled, leaving the *hibachi* standing forgotten where she had put it down. A slight breeze blew a few red-hot embers out on to a straw mat, which began to smoulder. Fortunately the night watchman noticed it and put out the fire, and took the pearl-decorated *hibachi* to the police.

They soon found out that it belonged to Chiko and it was clear that she had intended to set fire to the house. The un-

151

happy widow was taken to prison. It was of no avail to tell them how she had been swindled by the moneylender, how she had lived in poverty because of him, while he prospered and went on swindling people who trusted him.

The sentence was cruel. For attempted arson the widow was to die at the stake.

'Poor Chiko,' people said. 'What a strange world this is. She was always an honest woman who never did any harm.

But there's nobody who can get the better of Chogoro. His turn will come some day – how long have we got to wait, though?'

Ooka, too, had heard a great deal about the blameless life the widow led, as well as the bad reputation of the moneylender. Thinking it over he saw clearly that Chiko was speaking the truth and had been swindled and driven to her terrible deed by the moneylender who stole her money. Yet what could he do when

sentence had already been passed? Ooka decided to postpone the execution. The widow's sad fate allowed him no sleep. He kept seeing the triumphant look on the moneylender's face as Chiko was led, bound, to prison.

I will take a closer look at him, the judge thought to himself at last, and summoned Chogoro to appear before him without delay.

Chogoro did not want to go, but had no choice but to obey. He went slowly, as if his feet were hobbled.

'I have summoned you in connection with the case of the widow Chiko,' the judge said. 'A terrible end awaits her, as you know. Sentence has been passed but I want to be certain nothing has been overlooked. I must, therefore, make sure whether her statement that she had placed in your care five hundred gold pieces some years ago is true. Tell me honestly what happened. Did you do business with her, or not?'

Chogoro started, like a crotchety old clock. 'I can't remember, Your Honour,' he lied brazenly.

'You may have forgotten. I can't expect anybody to remember everything,' Ooka said. 'Search your memory once more. If you can't remember I know a powerful charm against forgetfulness.'

'A charm?' Chogoro asked with foreboding.

'I'll explain it to you,' Ooka smiled mysteriously. 'Friends taught me this charm when I was a young man but I never thought, then, that I would ever be a judge in Edo.'

'I have never heard of anything of the sort. How does it work?' Chogoro was curious to know.

'Don't be impatient, you'll soon know,' Ooka calmed him. 'Turn both your thumbs up and bring them together'. When the moneylender did so, the judge continued, 'Well done, now I will bind your thumbs together with a strip of rice paper. Like this, see? That's it. What are you grimacing for? It doesn't hurt. Just hold them like that for a moment. I will put my seal on it to make sure you don't tear the paper. That would spoil the effect of the charm. Now go home and when you remember your business with Chiko, come and tell me.'

The moneylender waited no longer; he bowed low and left quickly. He was pleased to have got off so lightly. Hardly had he left the court building, however, when he realised it was not going to be as easy as he had imagined. People pointed at him and turned around to stare. He tried to hide his hands in the wide sleeves of his kimono and hurried as fast as his feet would carry him. Every now and then somebody bumped into him nearly knocking him down but he managed to get home. To his servants' surprise he did not go into the front room to sit over his account books but went to the farthest room in the house announcing that he

153

was not at home to anybody that day. He told only his wife what had happened. She tried to comfort him but what good was that when she could not untie his thumbs?

When it was time to eat she had to feed him like a baby because he could not hold his chopsticks. Even worse, he had to go to bed with his clothes on, with the dirt and dust of the whole day on them.

Early next morning Chogoro went back to the courthouse.

'Why so early, Chogoro?' Ooka greeted him with a smile, in a very good mood. 'How did you sleep? What's the matter? You look troubled. Hasn't the charm worked yet?'

'Not one little bit, Your Honour,' the moneylender grumbled. 'Try as I can, I can't remember a thing. Your charm doesn't work on my bad memory. Please be so kind and untie my thumbs.'

'I can't do that, my dear Chogoro. I'd be a laughing stock if I didn't observe what I myself ordered. Go home and keep on trying. You'll find it'll work, even if it takes a bit longer.'

Chogoro was furious but did not dare say anything to the judge. He only bowed respectfully and shuffled off home with his thumbs still bound.

He might have endured it all, even not being able to swat at flies and mosquitoes, but what hurt him most of all was that his business was at a standstill. He kept no assistant because he grudged the money

and did not want anyone spying on his shady dealings. Now he was penalized for it. With his hands bound he could not even hold the brush to press his debtors for payment, nor could he hold his beloved abacus to see how his wealth had grown.

During the few days that Ooka was trying out his charm against forgetfulness on Chogoro, the moneylender changed unbelievably. He was thinner and his face was as pale as a corpse's. His wife pitied him and tried to persuade him: 'It's not worthwhile to torment yourself like this. Go and confess everything to Ooka. What can he do to you? At the most he will order you to pay Chiko's money back. That's nothing to you. You are rich enough to be able to afford it.'

Chogoro preferred to suffer rather than entertain the thought of having to pay back money he had once got hold of.

'Not on your life,' he ground his teeth, dashing about the room like a madman, his bound thumbs before him.

'Just consider the money you are losing because you can't do business,' his wife tried a different approach. 'You can see that Ooka is capable of letting you go on like this until you die. He is not a person to treat lightly.'

'I'd rather die than give those five hundred gold pieces back of my own will,' Chogoro stormed but with his thumbs bound he could not even bang the table to relieve his feelings. He was also afraid to shout too loudly in case the servants heard him. His wife had told him they already suspected something was wrong, whispering together, laughing and pointing to his room.

'What a life! The devil himself wished that Ooka on us. Why couldn't he have stayed in Yamada!' Chogoro hissed angrily.

He hung on with his thumbs bound together with the strip of sealed paper for another three days. On the fourth day, however, he set out again for the courthouse early in the morning.

'Oh, Your Honour, our wise and just judge,' he started, overflowing with politeness. 'From the moment you decided to try out your charm against forgetfulness on me and bound my thumbs, I have done nothing day and night but think back, but my stupid old head is no good. I just could not remember. So I thought of something else. I sat at my account books, my wife turned the pages for me and I checked every entry. Just imagine, Your Honour, I discovered that ten years ago I had accepted five hundred gold pieces from somebody. There was no name, but who else could it have been except Chiko, I said to myself, and tried to tap my forehead, but I couldn't do that with my thumbs bound, you'll agree,' Chogoro sighed with relief when he had finished.

'There, you see,' the judge nodded his head. 'I told you it was an infallible

charm. If ever you need to remedy forget-fulness again…'

'No, no, Your Honour. I'll never for-get anything for the rest of my life, if only you will untie my thumbs now.'

'Of course, there is no reason to have them tied together any longer,' said Ooka and cut the paper band. The moneylender quickly separated his thumbs as if he could not believe it was still possible. He would have jumped for joy like a small child, had he not been ashamed to do so.

Ooka summoned Chiko and all the witnesses.

'Now you admit,' he said, turning to Chogoro, 'that you had in your safekeep-ing five hundred gold pieces belonging to the widow Chiko?'

'Yes, I admit it,' the moneylender eagerly nodded his head. 'And I am wil-ling to pay them back.'

'Do you realize what harm you have done Chiko and how you abused her trust?'

'Yes, Your Honour,' answered Chogo-ro in a low voice.

'What interest do you charge your debtors?' the judge asked.

Chogoro looked at him in surprise. That was a question he had not expected.

'It depends, Your Honour, sometimes more and sometimes less,' he answered evasively.

'He demands ten percent a year,' somebody shouted.

'Ten percent? That makes fifty gold pieces a year and five hundred for ten years. The interest and the debt together amount to a thousand gold pieces. That is the sum you must pay to Chiko.'

It was agony for Chogoro to hear this, as if his bones were being broken under torture.

'Have mercy on me, Honourable Judge,' he cried desperately. 'It would beggar me to pay so much money out at once.'

'Who would have thought it?' the judge said sternly. 'The interest you charge must have brought you quite a fortune. You must return the money, you know that. Wait, we'll do it like this.' The judge turned to Chiko. 'How old are you?'

'Fifty-five,' the widow replied.

'Fifty-five,' repeated Ooka, thoughtfully. After a while he said, 'I pronounce the following sentence. This man

Chogoro will pay the widow fifty gold pieces at once as a fine for keeping back the money she had entrusted to him. Furthermore, he will pay back the amount owed in instalments of twenty-five gold pieces a year. That will take forty years. According to the law the sentence on Chiko cannot be carried out until after that time.'

That is how Ooka saved Chiko from a terrible death and taught Chogoro and others like him a lesson, that while Ooka was judge in Edo, no-one could swindle with impunity.

Ooka's Wisdom

NOTHING is as fickle as the favour of the mighty. Many of those at the Shogun's court had reason to know it. One day they would receive the highest honours only to be disgraced and forgotten the next day. Ooka seemed to be an exception. The supreme military ruler extended unfailing favour to him through-out the duration of his office in Edo, often summoning the judge to ask his advice on complicated matters.

'How do you manage so that nothing threatens your position?' Ooka was asked by his friends one day, when he had invited them to his house to sample a renowned autumn delicacy, fine crab

meat from Hokkaido. 'Can you tell us your secret so we can try it too, or do you want to take it with you to your grave?'

'I have no such secret,' Ooka replied, 'nor do I know of any reason to keep to myself anything that could be of advantage to others.'

'Then what is it? Will you tell us?'

'Of course, gladly. Wait until the servants open the doors, now we've finished eating, so that we can look at the full moon.'

Ooka's orders were soon carried out and the garden appeared before the guests in the silver light of the moon. It was an old belief that there was a white rabbit on the moon kneading dough for rice cakes. At that moment everybody felt as if they could really see the legendary animal on the round face of the moon. They were so engrossed in the lovely scenery that nobody noticed the maid entering to serve tea.

'What a beautiful night!' one of the guests exclaimed, breaking the silence. 'I can't imagine a better setting for your narration, dear friend Ooka.'

'You don't know if it will live up to

your expectations. You must decide for yourselves,' the judge answered, making himself more comfortable.

'Then start, we are all waiting impatiently,' said a middle-aged man sitting on the mat next to Ooka.

'It was not my intention to keep you in suspense. I only wanted you to enjoy the sight of Otsuki-sama (our Lady Moon) but it is time to begin now.'

Ooka cleared his throat and took a few sips of tea.

'You won't hold it against me, I hope, if I first ask you a question.'

'What can it be?' the guests wondered. 'Certainly nothing simple. Ooka will probably want to test us on the etiquette of the Shogun's court.'

'Do you agree?'

'Yes, yes!' came the answers from all sides.

'My first question is: Do you eat rice every day?'

'Of course! Who doesn't eat rice!' the guests answered, amused that the judge should ask such an obvious question.

'Can you tell me what rice tastes like?'

'What rice tastes like?' A man in black kimono with two family crests in white on the front, repeated the question, giving it a thought.

'Nothing special,' he said after a while. 'The taste is not important. The main thing is that it fills one's belly and stops one feeling hungry.'

'I quite agree with you,' Ooka nodded. 'I don't think anyone could describe it better. My next question is: Do you like the cakes with sweet fillings and the sweets made by the renowned confectioners of Edo?'

'Of course we do!' Ooka's friends laughed and looked at each other in amusement. 'It makes our mouth water just to hear about them.'

'I am not surprised,' Ooka agreed. 'Some of them really melt in one's mouth. Then why don't you eat them instead of rice, which, as you yourselves remarked, has no special taste and is useful only to fill our bellies?'

Who would waste time thinking about it, they all wondered, but did not want to say it aloud as they could not see what Ooka was aiming at.

'I think it's clear enough,' one of them at last decided to express an opinion. 'Isn't it said that there are two things a man can never have enough of? One is the beauty of a moonlit night, which we have convinced ourselves of a short while ago, and the other is the taste of well-cooked rice. We would soon get tired of eating nothing but sweet things.'

'Yes, that is so,' Ooka said with a smile. 'And that is the answer to the question you put to me earlier in the evening.'

Nobody could understand the judge's meaning. They had asked him how it was that the Shogun was always well disposed towards him, while others trembled that one wrong word might cost them their lives. Here he was, talking about sweets and rice! As if that had anything to do with the matter!

'What we have been talking about is more closely related to your question than you think,' Ooka told them, as if he had read their thoughts. 'You know well how many flatterers and toadies there are at the court of Edo, feeding the Shogun with their sweet words from morning to night. No wonder he soon becomes tired of them. Unlike them I prefer the truth.

It's quite ordinary and one doesn't tire of it. That is the similarity with rice. That is my secret,' said Ooka, adding: 'Now I can feel the cold air of night coming in from outside. It is time to say goodbye.'

The guests bowed with sincere respect for the judge and departed for their homes. They never forgot what Ooka told them that night and followed his advice with benefit to themselves.

A Sedan-Chair That Cost Too Much

ONE DAY, just as the clock was striking noon, two excited men came running to the courthouse. At first sight it was apparent that one was a wealthy citizen. His name was Tokubei and he had a china shop on the Ginza, one of the busiest streets in the town. The second man wore a workman's jacket and his hands were black from coal dust. He was Yotaro. He had been burning charcoal in the forests south of Edo all his life.

The two men demanded admission to Ooka immediately.

'What's the hurry? Your dispute won't run away,' the porter tried to pacify them and went to see if Ooka would receive

165

them. The judge agreed to hear them.

'What brings you here?' he asked them the usual question.

The charcoal burner wanted to begin but Tokubei interrupted him: 'I have done nothing wrong. I have acted within the law!'

'I'd like to see that law!' the charcoal burner shouted. 'Most likely you have invented it yourself!'

They kept on accusing one another and nothing would stop them.

Ooka listened for a while but try as he would, he could not understand what it was all about. Striking the little table in front of him with his fan he rebuked them: 'Enough of that, you will speak one by one when I address you, or I will punish you both. First you tell me your complaint,' the judge pointed to the charcoal burner.

'A thousand excuses,' the man bowed, 'but nobody, not even you, Your Honour, could ever have heard anything so ridiculous. The sky and the earth would have to change places if such mischief were to be tolerated. And he dares to say that it is lawful! I am a poor man and follow my poor reasoning, but...'

'What is all this about?' Ooka asked losing his patience. 'Will somebody finally tell me?'

'I will tell you at once, Your Honour, just let me recover a little.' The charcoal burner took a deep breath and started. 'I got up early this morning, before daybreak. I was about to make a fire so I could warm myself and make some tea, when I heard someone groaning. I must be imagining things, I thought, and carried on. Believe it or not, my lord, in a few moments the sighs and groans began again. That sounds like a human

being, I thought, I'd bet my life on it. Where could there be anyone in this wild place except for my wife and myself, and she was still fast asleep. I must go and see who it can be, I said to myself, and what did I see?' the coal miner stopped, wiped his forehead and looked at Ooka, as if to ask whether he should continue.

'Don't be afraid, go on,' Ooka urged him, listening carefully to every word.

'There I saw a frail old man sitting on the bare ground. You won't believe me, Your Honour, but I swear I am speaking the truth. The poor old thing wouldn't say anything at first, he was too ashamed, but at last he told me with tears in his eyes

that his own son Tokubei, that one there standing in front of you,' the charcoal burner pointed to his adversary, 'had brought him there and left him to his fate.'

Tokubei started waving his arms about wanting to interrupt the coal miner but Ooka stopped him saying, 'Yotaro is speaking now.'

'I could hardly believe my own ears but it was the truth,' the coal miner continued, becoming excited. 'I've got to do something about it, I said to myself. What would the world be coming to if children were allowed to get rid of their parents, who had given everything for them? I put the old man on a pushcart and took him back to his home. I know, Your Honour, that you will decide justly and that you will punish such a wicked son. Forgive me for troubling you.'

'Is that all?' Ooka asked.

'Yes, my lord,' the charcoal burner nodded politely. 'I would only like to add that I have never seen anything so cruel in my whole life, and that's three score years.'

'Now you will testify, Tokubei,' said Ooka, 'but first let me ask you a question.'

Tokubei, who had been preparing to reel off innumerable proofs of innocence, looked at Ooka in surprise.

'Do you have a son?' the judge asked him.

Tokubei nodded silently.

'Go and fetch him,' the judge commanded. 'We will adjourn until he arrives.'

It did not take long and the merchant returned with a sturdy youth of about fifteen. The boy looked around with curiosity and it was evident that he was not the least shy in the strange surroundings.

Only after his father nudged him did he kneel before the judge, touching the ground with his forehead.

'Now, Tokubei, it is your turn to tell us your side of the story,' the judge told the merchant.

'I am impatient to do so, if you allow me,' Tokubei started. 'I won't deny

anything as I have nothing to fear. I was only following the law.'

'Keep to the subject,' Ooka interrupted him.

'I am coming to it, Your Honour. It is true that I took my father to a lonely place in the forest. I am neither the first nor the last to do so. Who would think anything of it? My father is old and good for nothing. A year ago he was still all right. He could do a lot in the shop that he had passed on to me. He also helped to look after the children. Now, it's not worth talking about, he's just another mouth to feed. Well, we have a law, after all, that a family is not responsible for those of its members who are not of any use. I have, therefore, done nothing wrong and can't be punished, whatever Yotaro may think. You, Your Honour, are known to be the most just of all the judges that have ever walked on this earth. I am convinced that you will not sentence me.'

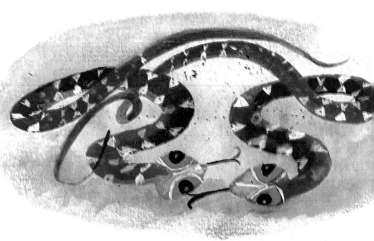

'I have no reason to,' Ooka assured Tokubei. 'On the contrary, because you have done what the law permits, as you say, I order you to take your father back to the forest, to the same place where you took him yesterday.'

'I knew, that you would see my point, Your Honour,' Tokubei's face lit up and he looked victoriously at the charcoal burner, who could not believe his ears.

'Who can afford to feed an extra mouth?!' Tokubei said. 'Business is bad and rice is more expensive every day.'

'I haven't finished yet,' Ooka continued. 'Before I let you go, you must promise to fulfil one condition.'

'What condition is that, Your Honour?' Tokubei asked in surprise.

'You will have your father carried to the forest in a sedan-chair of black lacquered wood, made especially for this purpose and lined with silk cushions so it will be comfortable for him.'

'Excuse me, my lord, but just think what such a chair would cost,' Tokubei protested. 'Why can't I take him there on the same old cart as before?'

'No,' Ooka said gravely. 'I realize it may seem expensive considering you're only going to use it this once, but in a family like yours, the chair can serve the next generation. Imagine how handy your son will find it when you become old and useless.'

'How long will I have to wait, my lord, before I'll be able to put my father in

a sedan-chair like that?' Tokubei's son asked promptly and at that moment he looked just as mean as his father.

'What d'you mean, you cheeky brat?' Tokubei turned angrily to his son, wanting to punish him on the spot. He stopped, seeing Ooka smiling as he watched them.

169

He scratched his head, embarrassed. He thought for a while and then said, 'When I think about it, Your Honour, the chair would be a waste of money. After all, I am not so badly off that I can't keep my father. With your permission I will let him stay at home and I promise I will look after him as best as I can.'

'As you wish,' Ooka nodded his head. 'I shall be glad to give my permission. I thank you, Yotaro, for not being indifferent to an old person's sufferings!'

Ooka had turned to the charcoal burner. 'If ever you need anything, don't hesitate to come to me.'

With those words Ooka closed the case. Yotaro returned to his charcoal furnace in the forest and Tokubei to his china shop.

Tokubei kept his word. He looked after his old father with great care to make up for having treated him so badly. His son learned from his father's example and the family lived happily for many, many years.

A Willow Tree as Witness

ONE MORNING when Ooka came to his office, he saw his new assistant, Yamaguchi, who had only recently begun working there, looking worried over some papers. He was so absorbed in his work that he did not notice his master enter. Only when Ooka spoke to him, asking what engrossed him, did he give a start and apologize for being so impolite as not to greet him.

'I would rather you told me what's troubling you. I may be able to give you some advice,' Ooka said to him.

'I am preparing the material for the case today and I am at a loss as to how proceed. There is no evidence here at all and

I just don't know what to do with it.'

'Really?' Ooka said with surprise. 'That does seem strange. Let me have a look at it.'

Ooka took the papers and went to his office. There he spread them out on the table and read them through carefully. At first he frowned, turning his head from side to side as if he did not know what to do. When he reached the last page, however, he said to himself with a smile, 'We'll take a good look at you, my fellow!'

He called out into the back room as if he could hardly wait to convict the

offender. 'Yamaguchi, I am leaving for the court room. Send Tarobei after me.'

'Yes, Judge, he will be there immediately. He has been waiting since early this morning.'

As Ooka took his seat, Tarobei was already kneeling respectfully before him with his head bent low. He wore a cotton jacket and dark close-fitting trousers. On his feet he had straw sandals. At first sight it was obvious that he was a peasant.

'Is your name Tarobei?' Ooka asked him.

'Yes, my lord,' the countryman raised his head. His suntanned face contrasted with those of the town-dwellers, proud of their pale complexion, untouched by the sun and the wind.

'Where do you come from?'

'From a village called Hazumi. It lies on the way to the Hakone Mountains.'

'What complaint brings you here before the court?'

'Last year, just as summer was starting and the rice fields were being weeded, I lent a man called Jirokichi three ryo and to this day he has not paid me back.'

'Where did this happen?'

'Where? You don't know the place at all,' the farmer answered simplemindedly, looking at Ooka.

'Never mind about that. Just describe it to me.'

'Hm, that won't be easy,' Tarobei scratched his head. 'I don't know how to begin. Well, it was just an ordinary path,

with fields on both sides, where the rice was green. The ears were beginning to form and it looked like being a good harvest. A sight for sore eyes! I only hoped no disaster would come to it.'

'Were you weeding or hoeing it?' Ooka asked.

'No, not that day. It was market day in the neighbouring town and they had a lottery. That's why I was going there. I had bought a lottery ticket and what do you think? I won!' Tarobei smiled with pleasure at the thought of it.

'How much did you win?'

'Three ryo, of course. I tied them carefully in a cloth and hurried home.'

'On the way you met Jirokichi, though, and lent him the money. Isn't that how it was?' Ooka went on.

'Yes, exactly as you say. How can you know that?' the peasant was surprised.

'What was Jirokichi doing there?'

'I don't know,' Tarobei shook his head. 'I only know he was standing behind me at the market and when I drew my lottery ticket, he saw I had won. Then he disappeared and I didn't see him again until we met on the field path as I was going home.'

'Did you address him or did he speak to you?' the judge wanted to know.

'Why should I speak to him, sir? I didn't even know him.'

'That means that he addressed you.'

'Yes, he said: "You've won three ryo, haven't you? That's exactly the amount

I need." And then...' the man stopped.

'Go on, tell me what followed.'

'Well, then he asked me to lend it to him and said that he would pay me back at the end of the summer, after the feast of the dead. Those were just empty words, judge,' Tarobei sighed. 'The feast

day went, then autumn came. Then the New Year came round and the spring, but there was no sign of Jirokichi. When the Boys' festival day drew near, I set out for his village, which is a long way from ours. I wanted him to give the money back but he said he didn't owe me anything and how dare I and threw me out. That made me really angry which is why I have brought my complaint to court.'

'Very well, Tarobei. That's enough for now. Have Jirokichi brought in,' Ooka made a sign to the court assistant.

Jirokichi came in at once. He wore a light grey yukata with a darker sash and his hair was tied in a tight knot on the top of his head.

'How do you earn your living?' Ooka asked.

'I have a few fields, Your Honour, but my main source of income is a little shop. Otherwise I would be as poor as a church mouse like the other villagers,' Jirokichi said confidently.

'Good, now let us get down to the matter in hand,' Ooka stopped him. 'As far as I know, you borrowed a sum of money from Tarobei, some time ago, and have not returned it although it is long over-due.'

'But, Your Honour,' Jirokichi protested, 'how can anybody want me to return something I have never borrowed?'

'Did he borrow three ryo from you or not, Tarobei?' the judge looked at the peasant.

'Yes, on the path between the fields that leads from our village to the neighbouring town. Exactly as I have told you!'

'What cheek! I have never borrowed anything from him. I don't even know where the place he's talking about is. I have never been there,' the shopkeeper said angrily.

'Tarobei, have you got a receipt?' Ooka asked.

'A receipt?' the farmer looked at the judge in surprise. 'We were in the middle of the fields. How could anyone write a receipt! To tell the truth it didn't even occur to me to want one. After all, he has much more money than I do. I thought he would soon pay me back!'

'There you have it,' Jirokichi cried. 'He hasn't even got a receipt. You'd hardly find a fellow anywhere who would lend money without keeping a receipt. He's just a thorough liar!'

'You call me a liar?' Tarobei exclaimed. 'Heaven above is my witness that I am speaking the truth.'

'A witness like that is not much good,' Ooka remarked. 'Was there anybody there besides the two of you?'

'No, there wasn't, Your Honour. Everybody was at the market.'

'Was there anything growing nearby?'

'There was rice growing there but that was harvested last autumn,' answered Tarobei.

'Are you sure there was nothing else?'

'I must think,' said Tarobei rubbing his brow.

'I know!' he suddenly cried out. 'There was a willow tree there, nice and green with long branches and it's still standing there.'

'A willow tree, you say. Well, it's not exactly an ideal witness but as we have no other we must be satisfied. Go and bring the willow to court as soon as you can!' Ooka told the peasant.

'You want me to bring a willow to court?' Tarobei could not believe his ears.

'Yes, you heard rightly. Now go so that we don't waste any more time,' Ooka ordered him.

There was nothing Tarobei could do but go.

Jirokichi laughed to himself. After all, a willow tree can't talk and a witness that can't speak is of no use. He felt confident that Ooka would not be able to convict him.

As they were waiting for Tarobei to return, Ooka suddenly said, 'Jirokichi, why don't you go and help Tarobei with the willow?'

'But, Your Honour, the place where it is growing is a long way from here. Tarobei can't have got there in such a short time.'

'Then you know where the willow is growing?' Ooka looked at him sternly. 'A short while ago you claimed you had never been there. Explain yourself!'

'Well, to tell the truth, Your Honour…' Jirokichi hesitated, losing his confidence.

'That's exactly what I want you to do. To tell me the truth,' Ooka interrupted him. 'Were you with Tarobei under the willow tree or not?'

'I was there but…' Jirokichi was now at a loss and unsure of what to say.

'If I find out when the witness arrives, and he will be here any moment, that you were lying, then you will not only have to pay back the sum you owe but you will also be accused of deceiving the court. That is a very serious offence. You'd better give it more thought. Tarobei must already be on his way back.'

'When all is said and done, three ryo won't kill me,' the shopkeeper sighed.

'Then you admit that you borrowed the money from Tarobei on that path in the fields and that the willow witnessed it?'

'Yes, I admit it,' Jirokichi said touching the ground with his head.

When Tarobei came stumbling into the court with the willow tree on his cart, the unusual witness was no longer needed. Jirokichi returned the money to him with interest.

That was the end of a court hearing which soon became known throughout the Japanese islands.

Ooka and the Pickpockets

At the time when this story took place, Ooka was already the supreme judge and administrator of Edo. He had done a lot of good for the town and the people were grateful to him. However, even the most just and popular men have enemies. There were people who were jealous of Ooka and the exceptional favour bestowed on him by the Shogun. They tried to find a way to discredit Ooka in the Shogun's eyes. Something soon turned up.

The pickpockets of Edo were behind it. They were a constant problem, threading their way through the streets of Edo night and day, practising their tricks at the expense of honest people. They were so expert at their 'profession' that they were very seldom caught in the act. They even had their own guild. If things looked bad they would stick together, warning each other and never betraying one another. No wonder that it was such a difficult problem.

This played into hands of Ooka's enemies. One day when one of them had been robbed, and the unknown thief had sent his empty moneybag back with a cheeky remark, he said to his friends: 'We hear so much praise for our judge.

They say there has never been another like him. As if that isn't enough, he himself proclaims that no culprit will escape him. That may be the truth but so far he hasn't had any success with the pickpockets. For a man as clever as he is, it should be child's play.'

Ooka's enemies put their heads together and decided that they would complain about the thieves and other things in the town to the Shogun himself, putting all the responsibility on Ooka. They did what they said they would, sending a letter to the Shogun, where they wrote:

YOUR HIGHNESS,

Edo, the biggest and most important town in the country, is the meeting place of pickpockets. Nobody is safe from them. They would steal the very nose off one's face. Their insolence has no bounds. They make fun of the local authorities.

We turn to you, Your Highness, with the most respectful request to order their criminal guild to be broken up and to order Judge Ooka, who is responsible for order in the town, to put an end to their activities.

With deepest respect
Your faithful subjects

Ooka's enemies submitted their request to the Shogun's office in the prescribed way. They knew that it was not so easy to complain, and they slipped a pouch full of gold pieces to the head of the office to make sure their letter would reach the Shogun quickly and that the official would put in a word for them. They hoped that Ooka would fail in the difficult task, what else could he do?

When the Shogun had read the letter from his faithful subjects, who preferred not to sign their names, he frowned and said, 'What can things be like in the town, when the people have to address such complaints to me?'

The Shogun never went among ordinary people and had no idea what things were like in the town. He therefore had no idea how difficult it was to deal with pickpockets.

'Call Ooka,' he ordered.

When the judge arrived the Shogun gave him the letter to read.

'Is it true?' he asked angrily, when Ooka had finished reading the letter.

'Yes, Your Highness,' Ooka replied calmly.

One of the Shogun's advisers, an enemy of Ooka, took advantage of the situation to make things worse for Ooka: 'Your Highness, surely the problem is that punishments for theft are too low and the rascals are not put on the rack or in the stocks to make them confess to everything.'

'What do you think?' the Shogun turned to Ooka.

'If I had to torture and execute everybody who steals a few coppers, Edo would soon be left empty,' Ooka replied without hesitation, and continued with a smile. 'It would also include those we suspect the least, because anyone who accepts a bribe, is, in fact, also a thief!'

A high official next to Ooka moved restlessly and wanted to say something but the Shogun stopped him and turned to the judge.

'What then do you suggest?'

'I beg Your Highness to keep me in your favour,' said Ooka, who realized from the tone of the Shogun's voice that the situation was serious. 'I will put everything in order to your satisfaction. I assure you that I will deal with the pickpockets immediately and those who deserve it will receive heavy punishment.'

'Very well, but remember that if you fail then you will lose *your* head, and not the thieves,' the Shogun said and gestured to show the audience was at an end.

That day Ooka did not go to his office but returned home. The moment he crossed the treshhold everyone could tell that he did not want to be disturbed.

He took a bath and putting on a light kimono sat on the verandah from where there was a pleasant view of the garden. Now that he was alone he saw the situation clearly. He was aware that the Shogun's anger could not be taken lightly. He sat for a long time, frowning, his brow wrinkled, fanning himself. Finally he rose and went into the garden. Here and there he absent-mindedly picked off a dead flower or a dry twig, but he still looked worried. Only when he came upon a small *Hokkaido* pine in an oval ceramic bowl did his face brighten. It was his favourite bonsai, a miniature tree, which his father had planted. He had bequeathed it to his son as a precious heritage. Not a day passed without Ooka devoting at least a few moments to its care. As he looked at it now, he saw in his mind's eye a mountain valley, where a bubbling brook became a waterfall and where on a steep slope a twisted pine like his tiny tree was bravely resisting the wind and the storms.

At that moment Ooka forgot all his worries and it seemed to him that he had nothing else to do but listen to the singing of the birds and watch the reflection of the sun restlessly flashing in the rapids of the stream.

After a while Ooka rose, took a small pair of scissors and began trimming the pine where it was too dense. At the same time he was thinking of a way to deal with the Edo pickpockets. He did not have much time. After all, the Shogun had said quite clearly what penalty threatened him if he did not take effective steps to deal with the pickpockets.

Deep in thought Ooka put the scissors aside and slowly followed the path of flat stones of different shapes. Suddenly he stopped. Just as he came to the garden lamp at a turn in the path he struck his head with his hand and exclaimed, 'I've got it!'

He went back into the house and called Naosuke, 'Quickly, prepare my sedan-chair, I am going to the office!'

The old servant ran to the porter's lodge where the sedan-bearers were drinking tea and resting. When they heard their master's order they jumped up quickly and hurried to the yard to prepare the sedan-chair. No sooner had they put candles in the lanterns, for evening was drawing near, when Ooka came out in his offical robes and sat in the chair.

Sharp cries of 'Get out of the way, get out of the way!' were heard. The sedan was carried quickly through the crowded streets of Edo. Before long Ooka entered the city courthouse in the South Town, and went straight to his office.

He could be heard dictating to the court clerk whose brush flitted over the paper as he neatly drew the characters setting down the judge's words.

'Make sure the notice is hanging up throughout Edo tomorrow morning at the latest,' Ooka ordered him.

The next day on every corner one could see people crowding to read a public notice such as they had never seen in their lives. That was saying something, for in those days public notices from officials of Edo were abundant, full of new orders for people to follow.

The notice read:

Let all pickpockets of Edo take notice!

The office of the esteemed Shogun Yoshimune (May he live a thousand years!) has been informed that members of the Guild of Pickpockets in Edo are carrying out their profession without paying any taxes as every guild member should and must. It has therefore been decided that any pickpocket who wants to exercise his profession in our town, whether masters, journeymen or apprentices, must carry an official licence for this activity. The fee is three coppers and the owners of such a licence will be able to carry on their activities without fear of punishment even if caught. Whoever robs the honourable and honest citizens of Edo without a licence will be beheaded without further trial as a warning to others. All members of the Guild of Pickpockets are requested to collect their licences, on payment of three coppers, on the sixth day of the next month at the Hour of the Horse. Ignorance of this notice is no excuse.

Ooka Tadasuke, Supreme Judge

When the people of Edo read it they did not know what to make of it. 'We deserve better treatment than this,' some said indignantly looking around carefully making sure they had not been overheard by anyone undesirable. 'The pickpockets will have an official licence to rob us at their pleasure!'

'That's all we need, added to all the taxes and fees we are already obliged to pay,' others sighed.

'We fools thought that Ooka was just,' the dyer, who left his shop to find out what the notice said, remarked bitterly.

'One of the pickpockets' influential protectors must have bribed Ooka to give in to them. I always say that those in power are not to be trusted!' the seller of wooden clogs said angrily.

'A thief! Catch the thief!' a voice in the crowd shouted.

'My purse is gone! All my today's earnings were in it.'

The master carpenter who had just been robbed thrust aside those standing near him and ran to catch the pickpocket, but he was already out of sight.

By the evening nobody was talking about anything else but the fact that pickpockets had official permission to rob people.

It was bound to reach the Shogun's ears. One of his courtiers whispered it to him with a fulsome smile.

'Wouldn't it be better to put an end to

Ooka's tricks once and for all?' he dared to add, and as a sign of his deepest respect and humility he fell on his knees before the Shogun, bowing his head to the ground.

The Shogun frowned angrily and would have ordered Ooka to come to him at once but then he thought of all the disputes which the judge had so wisely settled, though sometimes using very unexpected methods, and that set his mind at rest.

'I gave Judge Ooka Tadasuke a free hand in this matter,' he pronounced gravely. 'We must therefore wait. I wish nobody to interfere.'

There was a great uproar among the pickpockets, too. They couldn't understand what Ooka's motives were. Things went so far that they got no pleasure when they managed to pull off one of their tricks.

Their guild master, Kinzo, was worried, too. An official licence for professional pickpockets? Who had ever heard of such a thing, he wondered, shaking his head doubtfully. Does Ooka intend to make honourable citizens of us for robbing other people? Surely not. There must be snag in it, somewhere.

However he looked at it, Kinzo could not find an answer. Come to think of it, such a licence would not be so bad. I'd better call the guild together, so we can discuss it. Two heads are better than one.

Kinzo sent for his most experienced assistant, Sanji, and told him to let all the members of the guild know that next day, immediately after the second night watch, there would be a special pickpockets' meeting at the usual place. Sanji set out at once for the market and all the places where he knew he would find his comrades. He whispered to each of them stealthily and soon the word got round. They all promised to come, for they, too, were anxious to solve the mystery.

The meeting took place in West Ryogoku, a quarter where circus artists, jugglers, wrestlers, strolling players and the poor of Edo lived. There were old, deserted temples there and inns, which even the police did not dare enter at night.

As the hour of the second night watch drew nearer, the courtyard of the sanctuary slowly filled with people who moved as silently as shadows.

It was, indeed, an usual sight. Pickpockets always try to mingle with the crowd unnoticed, so it had to be an important event for them to gather in one place where the Shogun's bailiffs could catch them like mice in a trap before one could snap one's fingers. That was why some of them waited in the shadows of the trees surrounding the temple to make sure the air was clear.

Experienced old hands of the profession only then decided to go in. Although greyhaired and getting on in years, they were still active. With them came their

apprentices, known as greenhorns, who were quite terrified.

The pickpockets wore cotton garments or short kimonos like most simple people of Edo. Their trade made it necessary for them to be inconspicuous and did not allow eccentricities of dress. Only a gleam in their eyes would betray them to an observant watcher.

Clouds began to gather over the evening sky and the guildmaster ordered his assistant to light a few lanterns. In their dim light the gathering looked more like a collection of ghosts than people of flesh and blood.

Kinzo, a thief above all thieves, for how else could he be a guildmaster, was of a smaller build than most pickpockets. His face, however, expressed resolution and authority. When he lifted his hands as a sign for the discussion to begin, his sleeves fell back showing his arms covered in blue tattooing, as was customary among the Edo underworld.

'You all know why we have gathered here,' he said. At that moment the clouds

opened and the white light of the moon lit up the temple courtyard. Some of the pickpockets covered their faces in fear.

Was this a bad sign? they wondered. Are the heavens themselves showing us up? Although they were not easily frightened, they started looking around furtively, gooseflesh on their arms, fearing that guards would suddenly appear behind them to lead them to prison or even to the gallows, but all was still.

'Who has got anything to say?' Kinzo broke the stillness. True, everybody was expecting the question but nobody wanted to be the first to raise his hand. After a short while a young pickpocket in the first row, his hair tied in a bun, plucked up courage.

'Speak, Magoshichi,' Kinzo bade him.

'We all know why Ooka wants to get us to come to the court,' Magoshichi began. 'Once we are there, he will have us locked up without much ado, and we won't get out unscathed.'

'He is right!' could be heard all around. 'We won't be taken in. We're not going anywhere!'

'That sounds easy enough,' a grey-haired man in a blue tucked-up cotton kimono remarked. 'The notice says in black and white that anybody caught stealing without an official licence will be executed without mercy. Who wants to be a head shorter, I'd like to know?'

'Nobody!' cried the thieves, some involuntarily touching their necks, to make sure their heads were still sitting tight.

The discussion began to get more heated. The pickpockets all wanted to have their say. Everyone expressed his opinion but they could not agree. The guildmaster sat quietly on his elevated place listening carefully and not a word escaped him. When in their enthusiasm they forgot their caution, waving their arms about and shouting and arguing, Kinzo rose energetically and cried, 'Quiet!'

The pickpockets were immediately quiet.

'That's quite enough,' the guildmaster said. 'It is high time to decide what to do tomorrow!'

Kinzo surveyed the tense faces of the thieves gathered there and said, 'Some think the notice is a trick, while others are convinced that we can trust Ooka. I have thought it over carefully, and I am sure he will not send us to prison if we do what he demands. If he didn't keep his promise, nobody would believe his public notices.'

The pickpockets whispered among themselves in agreement.

'I suggest we obey the notice. It will mean confessing to earning our living in a dishonest way but he can't punish us without any proof. Every child knows that without proof our judge has never sentenced anybody yet,' Kinzo stopped.

This time not a sound could be heard from the gathering. They were all

hanging on the guildmaster's words for his decision would affect the course of their lives.

'Ooka has promised an official licence for our trade as pickpockets for the price of only three copper coins,' the guildmaster continued. 'What more can we wish for?'

'Yes, yes, Kinzo is right,' the pickpockets nodded in agreement.

'I therefore order you all to appear at the court as one man tomorrow that is the sixth day of the month, at the Hour of the Horse,' the guildmaster continued. 'Let everybody bring three copper coins with him. Whoever fails to come will cease to be a member of our guild.'

When Kinzo had said this and before the gathering realized it, he disappeared with his attendants within the ruins of the temple. That was the signal for others to leave. The pickpockets dispersed in all directions, looking around to see if they could find a victim in the dark streets to rob him without an official licence as yet.

'Things will be quite different tomorrow!' they said and many thought their profession would lose its charm when there would be nothing to fear.

On the day assigned in the public notice the pickpockets began to assemble at the courthouse. They dressed for the occasion, there is no doubt about it, but it was obvious at once that they felt uncomfortable and that they would rather have not been there.

'Sir, they are here!' Aikawa, a young court official broke into the judge's office, against all the codes of good behaviour. 'What a crowd there is! Who would have guessed there were so many pickpockets in Edo!'

'Everything prepared as I ordered?' Ooka asked.

'Yes, Your Honour,' Aikawa replied, smiling slightly and hoping Ooka would not notice, because he would disapprove. He always emphasized that when on duty one did not show one's feelings, but how could Aikawa refrain from smiling when he thought of what was going to follow?

Exactly at the Hour of the Horse the court gates were opened and the porter let one pickpocket enter after another, all in good order. The official sitting at a desk wrote down the nickname of each one as well as their real names. One was called One-eyed, another Six-fingers and yet another Crooked-tooth. Then there was one called Faint-heart and immediately after him came Blunderbuss scowling and looking ready to break out.

When the official procedure was finished, everybody had to pay three copper coins. The pickpockets were loath to part with them. They pulled them out of their moneybags slowly and unwillingly, and no wonder! All their lives they had been accustomed to dipping their hands into other people's pouches more often than into their own.

Finally the official placed a document

before each thief, bearing the words: I declare that as from today I will always carry an official licence. If I am caught in the act without it, I will be beheaded without a court hearing.

To be beheaded, that did not sound too good to any of them but what could they do? Everybody who wanted to keep his head had to sign the document. Those who could not write had to press their middle finger on this most important document.

When they had all taken their turn at the official's desk Ooka commanded the official licences which would make respectable citizens of the pickpockets for the first time since the world came into being, to be brought in.

The door opened and carriers specially employed for the occasion entered. They entered in pairs bearing between them large red signboards of oak. On each was a beautifully executed inscription: Officially licenced pickpocket.

Ooka ordered each thief to come up to him so that he could hang the sign around his neck. The first were so surprised that they complied, but the others soon realized they had been tricked. When they remembered what they had signed they turned as green with range as young rice shoots. A pickpocket with this sign around his neck would be more conspicuous than a three-headed devil! The gods alone knew how they could manage to steal then.

193

So the pickpockets let the licences be and took to their heels. They disappeared not only from the courthouse, but also from Edo, and thanks to Ooka and his wisdom the town was free of them for a long time.

How Ooka Decided Who Was the Best

TIME flies like a white horse seen through a crack in the door, is an old saying of the Japanese islands. It is true too. The years passed by and from one day to the next, without a rest, Ooka carried out his duties as a judge to the best of his ability. He was rightly esteemed far and wide, and the Shogun often turned to him for advice when he had an important decision to make. He knew he could depend on the old judge in all matters and respected him for his prudence and wisdom.

It came to pass that one day he wanted to appoint someone to head the supreme office of finance. This was a most import-

ant office because the state of the Shogun's treasury depended on it. The three most capable were finally chosen out of the large number of applications. The difficulty was that they were all outstanding experts and the wooden beads of the abacus flew under their fingers with tremendous speed.

Which of them was the best? That was a question nobody else could answer except Judge Ooka. How well he knew people! After all, he was in contact with them daily at court and knew all their weak points. Of those Ooka came into contact with one would be niggardly, another a squanderer, the third one lazy, the fourth so hard-working that he almost worked himself to death, the fifth a great talker and the sixth one would hardly utter a word. To put it simply, they were all different and no one was perfect.

Ooka never condemned anybody out of hand for their errors but tried to find the key to their behaviour and their deeds.

When it became necessary to choose between three applicants for the post of administrator of the supreme office of finance, the Shogun called Ooka to him and said, 'Test them and choose the most capable one. I will leave you alone with them and listen hidden behind a screen.'

Ooka promised to do his best and ordered the applicants to call in.

They appeared at once, for they had been waiting in the antechamber since early that morning, to learn which of them had been chosen by the Shogun. They were surprised to see Ooka, but did not let it show. They only bowed low and waited for the judge to address them.

'My Lord, His Highness the Shogun, has ordered me to test your knowledge of mathematics. Let us not waste time.'

The judge pointed to the first one and said, 'What figure will we get if we multiply eight by three?'

The man had been prepared for a complicated arithmetical task, and answered without hesitation, 'Twenty-four.' What

a question! he thought, Ooka must know as much about arithmetic as a six-year-old. Why he should be the one to examine us is beyond reason!

Ooka nodded and turned to the second one.

'Tell me what forty-nine divided by seven is?'

197

'Seven,' came the answer even before Ooka had finished speaking.

Now it was the third one's turn, the last of the applicants.

'I want you to tell me what two hundred divided by two is,' Ooka said.

The man waited until Ooka had finished asking the question, then he nodded, pulled his abacus from the wide sleeve of his kimono, and started counting. The others looked on in amazement.

What's happened to him?! they thought. He must have forgotten everything in his fear. What a fool he is making of himself.

In a short while Bunsho, for that was his name, looked up from the abacus and said, 'One hundred.'

'I am satisfied,' Ooka declared, and gestured for them all to leave.

'What decision have you come to?' the Shogun asked with unconcealed curiosity once they were alone.

'The last applicant is the man Your

198

Highness needs,' Ooka replied. 'It is true that they are all excellent mathematicians but we knew that beforehand and there was no need to test them. The first two could not see beneath the surface of things. Bunsho realized that there was more to it than doing a sum any small child could. He knew that to answer such a simple question at once, as his two companions did, he would make the one who was asking it look ridiculous. He showed that he was not only polite but also very tactful. I am convinced, Your Highness, that he will carry out his duties to your full satisfaction.'

It was as Ooka said.